THE TASTE
OF STRAWBERRIES

by
LINDA MUIR

CON-PSY PUBLICATIONS MIDDLESEX

First Edition
2003

© Linda M.Muir

Published by

CON-PSY PUBLICATIONS
P.O. BOX 14,
GREENFORD,
MIDDLESEX, UB6 0UF.

ISBN 1 898680 32 9

INDEX

	PAGE
CHAPTER 1 - - -	4
CHAPTER 2 - - -	7
CHAPTER 3 - - -	10
CHAPTER 4 - - -	13
CHAPTER 5 - - -	16
CHAPTER 6 - - -	18
CHAPTER 7 - - -	22
CHAPTER 8 - - -	26
CHAPTER 9 - - -	31
CHAPTER 10 - - -	34
CHAPTER 11 - - -	38
CHAPTER 12 - - -	41
CHAPTER 13 - - -	45
CHAPTER 14 - - -	47
CHAPTER 15 - - -	50
CHAPTER 16 - - -	53
CHAPTER 17 - - -	56
CHAPTER 18 - - -	59
CHAPTER 19 - - -	62
CHAPTER 20 - - -	65
CHAPTER 21 - - -	68
CHAPTER 22 - - -	71
CHAPTER 23 - - -	75
CHAPTER 24 - - -	78
CHAPTER 25 - - -	81
CHAPTER 26 - - -	84
CHAPTER 27 - - -	88
CHAPTER 28 - - -	91
CHAPTER 29 - - -	95
CHAPTER 30 - - -	98
CHAPTER 31 - - -	102
CHAPTER 32 - - -	105
CHAPTER 33 - - -	109
CHAPTER 34 - - -	113
CHAPTER 35 - - -	116
CHAPTER 36 - - -	120
CHAPTER 37 - - -	124
CHAPTER 38 - - -	127
CHAPTER 39 - - -	130
CHAPTER 40 - - -	133
CHAPTER 41 - - -	136

CHAPTER 1

There's around six thousand million people in the world. The more you think about it, the more you realise it's hard to stand out in a crowd like that. Yet we'd all like to leave our marks, I suppose. Like everyone else, I like to feel I'm important in the scheme of things. So how come I can never find a car parking space when I need one? Maybe it's just modern life putting me in perspective.

Anyway, that's how my saga got started - not being able to park the car when I needed to. I'd taken a whole precious Saturday and allocated it to buying Tom's niece's wedding present. It had to be purchased for the following week and I'd travelled all the way to Edinburgh to get something special. When it looked like I was going to have to go the sixty miles back home because there was nowhere to leave the car, my whole world was ending. Panic was about to break through the sea wall of my control. The universe was blatantly denying my significance. I was as nothing. Adrenaline tingled in my brain.

Then I heard it. 'You didn't ask the parking fairy.' Nothing more.

'What?' I said to my steering wheel.

'The parking fairy,' growled the gears as I crashed them into reverse. 'You didn't ask her to book you a place beforehand.'

'Oh, doesn't she do retrospective bookings then?' said I, moving off again in reluctant first.

'Try it and see.'

I turned cautiously left to see a red Escort backing out of a space and yes! It was mine.

With a tug on the handbrake and a sigh of relief, I decided there might be something to this parking fairy. Maybe someone was keeping an eye out for me after all. Maybe I was just a tiny bit important, and someone like me could stand out among a billion or two. That was my first experience of Sybil.

Later on, I said a mental thank you to the parking fairy.

'You can call me Sybil if you like,' came the reply, 'but I'm not really the parking fairy. You are.'

'Come again?' I thought. Now this conversation was truly underway, I imagined that the voice in my head had a face and a form - like everybody's mother with blond, set hair and a pained expression.

'It's quite straight forward,' she said with a sigh, flicking something imaginary from her cuff. 'Think about it. As soon as you feel a situation is under control, you start to feel more positive about it. Don't you?' She seemed to raise an eyebrow. 'You proceed more slowly and you look more carefully for the opportunity that you are sure is waiting for you. And because you are going more slowly and looking more carefully, you find it.'

'So, I'm my own parking fairy?'

'I told you it was straight forward,' Sybil replied with a slightly superior smile. 'Lesson One: Slow down, think positive and observe. Then you will receive what you need.'

'Where from?' I asked.

'The Universe of course!' said her disappearing voice. 'Where else could it come from?' I shrugged my shoulders. Maybe I could feel more in harmony with everything if I slowed down, thought positive and observed.

So I gave sauntering down to Princes Street my best effort, lingering at shop windows as I went. I insisted to myself that the right present was just waiting for me to buy it, and that if I'd just take time to look the whole day would be successful. I promised myself not to do my usual manic scamper.

Two hours and a visit to Jenner's later, I had two large bags of cushions and a matching throw for Gemma in the colour scheme she had talked about. It was comfortable in a childish short of way to think that however large it was, the Universe had somehow provided for me and looked after me. Could Sybil be right?

Safely home again, I made a cup of tea and put my feet up. Shopping-wise it had been a successful day, but it had been a long one. If it's just me against a billion, working to get the better of the world, it seems like too much of a struggle, I decided. Maybe I'd give Sybil's approach a go. I'd try and work with the world instead of competing against it. So as I finished my tea and stretched out in front of the fire. My next attempt at being observant was to ask the question, 'Where am I in this map of humanity?' It was a difficult question to answer when I didn't seem to have any co-ordinates.

True to form, I avoided the unanswerable question and started to think of something else. I remembered an old friend telling me about her family. I asked about her grandson. 'So who's Ricky like?' I said.

'He's not like anyone,' she replied. 'He's like himself.'

That reply made me feel a bit uncertain at the time and the uncertainty returned to me now. The new observant me noticed that I'd fallen into a trap - seeing people in terms of other people. No sooner would I get to know a new person, than I'd think of them as thinner than this one, richer than that one, more patient than the other and so on. Why couldn't I just see them as themselves, I wondered. Maybe it was easier to file them away between one friend and another in a kind of social filing system. Easier than getting to know what they were really like.

Mulling things over that evening, I realised I treated myself the same way. In the interests of self improvement, I'd take a long hard look at myself. What did I see? Well, I'm older than this one, more confident than that one, less successful than the other .... It's as if when I tried to look at myself, I saw all of the people I have ever known instead - I didn't see me at all. The comparisons were like smokescreens and the real me was nowhere to be seen.

Sybil interrupted my pensive flow, 'Are you hiding, or do you just not want to see yourself?' I realise now that I always felt at home with her. It didn't feel strange talking to this voice in my head.

'Of course I'm not hiding,' I replied defensively. 'What would I want to hide for?'

If you can feel a long, hard stare coming from nowhere in particular, I was feeling it.

'So who are you anyway?' she retaliated. I felt it would be better if I could describe myself - identify a few details - that sort of thing. 'My name is Laura, I'm forty five, married to Tom.' I paused. 'I'm a course coordinator in college, I like DIY and love my dogs ....' I tailed off. Surprisingly enough, that's quite a demanding thing to do. I could think of a list of adjectives that applied to me, but as soon as a word came to me I'd start using it to calculate my 'value' and edit it out again. It was as if I had got to compare myself to all the rest before I could be worth anything. I could feel the urge to be impressive, to compare and contrast with the competition. To wipe out all comers.

'I'm ...' I continued. Sybil wasn't even pretending to listen.

'I thought so. What you need is a new approach.'

'What? I'm doing my best.' I was defensive again.

'I am incomparable!' came the reply.

'What?'

'I am incomparable. Repeat it and believe it,' she said. 'No more comparisons are allowed. From now on, there is no measuring up. You're not better. You're not worse. You just are. Is that clear?' She was inquisitive and commanding like an old fashioned Matron.

Cowed a little, I ventured a question, 'I just am what?'

'Nothing. You just exist. No status - no shame, is the name of the game.' She was enthusing now. 'Think of all the anxiety you will be letting go of. Think of all that pressure to be something you're not ... it's just disappeared! Think of that list of things you said you must do before a target time ... it's just evaporated!' It sounded tempting. 'Doesn't it feel strange just to be you?' I could feel the stare again. 'Does it?'

Surprisingly after that tirade, she had caught my curiosity. What would it feel like? I wanted to get hold of that feeling and remember it. It would be a new approach and a new attitude. It was tempting to leave timescales and targets behind, to forget the latest initiative and let the competition come first.

'You don't know where you fit in to the rest of that billion and you haven't time to find out. But you have the chance to start a new adventure,' said the voice. 'You are about to begin to learn what it is like to be one individual (you) ... in a billion.' I was intrigued.

CHAPTER 2

Of course, being intrigued was one thing. Actually doing something about it was another. Armed with my instruction 'Slow down, think positive and observe', and my mantra 'I am incomparable ' my homework was just to 'be'. It took me about a week to find some free time. During the days in between, there were no direct interruptions from Sybil, but I did feel just the occasional encouragement to think before I reacted. And to watch what was happening around me. When I slowed down, I noticed that if I gave my colleagues a little more time to have their say, they usually gave me more of their listening time too. It was a kind of trade off, and when I allowed it to happen, stress levels fell. It was a good beginning.

Mid afternoon the phone rang at work. 'Hello, Laura? It's Sheila from Recruitment. That nightschool class I talked you into taking...'

'The Counselling one?'

'The numbers we've got won't justify it. The boss says don't run it. Is that OK?'

'You mean it's cancelled?'

'Yep. You've got Tuesday nights off from now on. Just think of it as a bonus.'

I laughed and hung up, wondering if the cancellation was my fault until I remembered I was supposed to be thinking positive. And I did feel relieved in a way. This was my opportunity to slow down as per instructions.

So there I was with a free evening and I was feeling foolish. Sybil said, 'Just be.' I felt awkward.What was I supposed to do?

'Nothing.'

I sat curled up in the armchair and gazed out of the window. 'But how can I do nothing? I am sitting and gazing. That's doing something, isn't it?' Now that I was thinking directly at her, Sybil's presence came into focus.

'And you're slouching too. That won't do.' She was in sergeant major mode. 'That chair's too comfortable. Get a straight-backed, hard bottomed chair. One of those kitchen chairs will do fine.' Impelled into the kitchen, I could see this was going to be fun all the way.

'Now that you're here, you might as well stay,' she said. I moved the chair until its back was towards the kitchen radiator, and sat down. 'Close your eyes and become aware of your breathing,' she said.

'Why?'

'Because it's a simple way of cutting out distracting visual impressions, and listening to your own breathing focuses your attention on you. OK?' I wouldn't dare disagree.

'Now just be. It's easy.'

And so it was. For about a minute, that is. I sat there nice and quiet, not comparing me to anybody, just being me. And then it started. I went charging off thinking about anything and everything - whether I closed the lounge window, could I re-write the Counselling course, should I send Helen flowers for her birthday, what will be the outcome of the next election. I really mean anything and everything. It was crazy. All I wanted to do was become aware of myself, and now the world and its trivia came gatecrashing into my thoughts. The more I tried not to think, the more thoughts sprang to mind.

'Sybil. I can't do this,' I wailed.

'Life Is A Haystack.' She was at work again.

'You're being enigmatic,' I complained.

'Not at all dear. I know how you feel. The world is tumbling in on you. There's too much information coming at you. And somewhere, like a needle in a huge haystack is you. Well, now is your chance to work your way out to the top of the stack and get a better view of what's going on.'

'I sounds great Syb, I just can't do it.'

'Of course you can. Today I am your guardian angel. Let me show you how. Remember, you are thinking positive.' She was wreathed in smiles. I hated her.

'Sybil, I've just told you I can't '

'You are going to calm down and have a look at what's going on in the inside of you rather than what's happening on the outside of you. Put on some soft music. Relax!' beamed the angelic being. 'Maybe I should have started you off this way. Sometimes I take too much for granted. You've got the room, the upright chair, some soft music and no interruptions. Now listen to me while I explain.'

I put on some soft music and listened. 'Now the music's on, it will drown out annoying background noise. Now, there's no one about. Sit comfortably in the chair so that you can feel your thighs being supported by the seat, and your back held by the chairback. OK?' I nodded. 'Make sure your feet are flat on the floor and that your hands are resting in your lap. Great. Let the music wash round you.' It did. I was still doing plenty, but my mind was fairly vacant and I wasn't unhappy as she continued.

'Close your eyes. Now I'm going to tense and relax you a bit at a time. You'll soon feel the benefit. Take your attention to your feet. Tense them up. Hold for a moment and then release the tension. Now think about your calf muscles. Tense them, hold, and release. Now move to your thighs. Tense the muscles. Hold it. Now release the tension.' After each instruction, she paused to let me feel the relaxation in that part of my body. It was good - I continued to do as I was told.

8

'Pull in your tummy muscles. Hold, and release. Now tense your chest muscles. Hold, release. Now your arms - tense, hold, release. Clench your fists. Hold, release. Raise your attention to your neck muscles. Tense them. Hold and release. Now screw up your face - hold and relax.' Sybil's voice, slow and smooth, caressed my mind into a warm sleepy state - like dozing on a warm summer beach.

'You can feel that lovely relaxed feeling throughout your body, can't you? As the music plays, feel that the music is massaging you softly. Feel more and more relaxed. Stay like this until the end of the track .... or for as long as you like.'

I can't tell you how that conversation ended, because I fell asleep and dozed long after the disc was finished. When I awoke, I felt rested. It didn't matter that my 'homework' wasn't finished. I felt better in myself. That was good progress.

I was also aware that I was less tense than usual and then (funnily enough) how tensed up I had been. I suppose you only miss that kind of tension when it's gone! Well, it was certainly going, and in that way at least I was learning about and becoming more aware of myself.

CHAPTER 3

I must have had five or six more attempts at the relaxation exercise before I could stay awake until the end of the music. I was delighted! 'Hey, Sybil! I'm still here,' I thought out to her. The returning feeling was faint, but it was one of approval. She carried on as if there had never been a break.

'Become aware again of your head, your neck, your chest and then your stomach. Be aware of your thighs, your calves and then your feet. Wiggle your toes. Stretch your arms a little. Then open your eyes slowly and stretch more if you feel like it,' she said. 'Congratulations. You have just taken time out for you. Don't be put off by the simplicity of this exercise. It's the first step in getting to know you again - don't rush it. Instead, make time to practise this every day for a week. When you notice yourself tensing up in some part, make it even more tense and then relax it again. The aim is simply to remember what it is like to be relaxed - go for it!!'

I did.

I worked at ten minutes' worth of relaxation every day until I found myself looking forward to my 'time out'. I was eager to feel the tension in my neck, shoulders and lower back just ebb away. Each time my goal was to reach what I called the comfort zone. I liked it so much I made the attempt to remember clearly what it felt like to be that comfortable. Then before I knew it, when I began tensing up during the rest of my day I'd find myself thinking, 'No, I want to feel more comfortable than that,' and I'd consciously relax the tensed up part until I felt at ease again. Result? Fewer headaches and more patience. I might not be one in a billion yet, but at least I knew myself a little better and (yes) I loved myself a little better too - every time I listened to what my body was telling me.

'So far the conversation has been all one way,' said Sybil at the end of one session.

'What do you mean?' I asked. 'What conversation?'

She sighed. 'I thought you were learning to be perceptive and aware!'

'Never mind, teaching me is your challenge in life,' I retorted. 'What conversation?'

'You and your body. Yes?' She peered into my eyes as if looking to see if there was any recognisable life form behind them.

'OK. So who's saying what?' I would not be put off.

'You have been listening to your body. You know, becoming aware of how it's feeling. Once you know how it's feeling, you adjust. Like a soldier taking orders.'

'I can relate to that,' I said pointedly.

'So the communication has been a bit one way, wouldn't you agree?'

'You mean it's the soldier's turn to give the orders?' She nodded. 'That sounds fine.'

'You've been listening carefully to what your body's telling you. And you've reacted. Now we're going to turn that on its head. You're going to talk to your body, and it's going to react.'

'How?'

'Let's just go through the same old routine. You know, get yourself comfortably seated. Close your eyes. Become aware of your breathing. Then slow it and deepen it slightly.' Sybil rattled off the instructions and I was surprised at how easy it was now to achieve the state she asked for. Maybe practice does make perfect after all. 'Now,' she began to speak more slowly, 'take yourself through the relaxation exercise just like you normally do.' I tensed and relaxed my muscles methodically from toe to head. Sybil gave me time just to experience the relaxation once more. 'That's good,' she said reassuringly. Now check out your body once again to see which parts have tensed up when you weren't looking. Relax them again.' There was another pause.

'This time, I want you to let your awareness range over your body until it finds what I'm going to call 'an area of discomfort'. It might be an ache or a twinge,' she went on, 'nothing very serious. See if you can find such an area.'

I imagined my mind was like a spotlight and let it play on me as I looked for discomfort. My left foot is where I stopped. I'd broken it years ago by falling off a ladder. It had healed very well and I'd almost forgotten about it. But when I walked a lot it ached in a tired sort of way. I chose to focus on that.

'Found something?' she asked. I nodded. 'Good. Just bear it in mind for a moment. In the meanwhile,' she added, 'I want you to think of the colour of love. It can be any colour you like.' I chose a gentle lilacy - pink. 'Now imagine that colour as a soft light. Surround yourself with that light for a moment or two.' It was gentle and soothing. 'Good,' she said again. 'Now I'd like you to take that beautiful light with you as you turn your attention again to your area of discomfort. Lovely. Now let that light the colour of love shine gently. Let it shine right through the part of you that is the area of discomfort. If your mind wanders, that's OK. Just bring it back again and watch how that area feels as it's wrapped up in the colour of love.' She stopped for a moment. 'Now ask yourself what that feels like.'

At first my foot felt sorer. I could feel pain pulsing through it. 'Remember this is the colour of love. Just let it work for you.' As the minutes passed, the pulsing began to ebb away. The pain became vaguer and all but disappeared. I felt quite pleased with myself.

11

After a couple of minutes (well, that's what it felt like), Sybil asked me to thank myself for caring for my body and to let the light gently fade away. Once again I was aware of my relaxed state, and gradually I brought myself back to my everyday self and opened my eyes again.

Sybil was stretched out on my sofa. 'Well,' she said, looking very pleased with herself. 'How did your foot feel?'

'How did you know I was concentrating on my foot?' I asked.

'Did it heat up a bit first?' She could be exasperating sometimes.

'Yes, but then it cooled down.' I thought about it again. It felt quite comfortable.

'So do you think your body got the message?'

'I don't know,' I said. 'I'm not sure.' I didn't want to be carried along on the strength of a few gentle thoughts. It would be too easy. 'Maybe.' I watched her to see what she would say next.

'Stay with maybe,' she said. 'Maybe's sensible and you should always be cautious in your experiences. But don't cast it aside,' she added as she sat up and got ready to stand. Add that on to your relaxation exercise and we'll see how you get on with it.' She brushed herself down. 'You shouldn't let those dogs up on the sofa, you know.'

'What exactly is the 'it' I'm to get on with?'

'Self healing,' she said over her shoulder, and was gone.

'I'd call it auto suggestion,' Tom said later when I told him about it.

'But does it work? That's what I want to know,' I said as we dried the last of the dishes, wondering why we never got round to buying a dishwasher.

'Well, it seems to do for some people. It's used for all sorts of conditions - pain relief, recovery from operations, blood pressure, that sort of thing.'

'I think my foot is easier.' I was hesitant as I spoke, in case he thought I was being foolish or over-imaginative.

'Then what does it matter what it's called?' he said with infuriating logic. 'Coming to walk the dogs?'

I absently folded the tea towel and put it on the rail. 'Yes,' I said. 'you're right.'

CHAPTER 4

It was summer - a time for the long holiday and dreaming of working part time. I'd been pulling out weeds from around the patio. Dried by the sun, they had yellowed, and the pile looked like a miniature haystack. I'd done the slowing down, was working on the positive thinking and still had a lot of observing to do. I wondered whether I was any nearer the top of my own particular haystack than I was when Sybil first goaded me into relaxation. 'A couple of straws up, or so.' It was Herself again. 'Once you've tidied those weeds away, you'll be about ready for your next challenge.' It wasn't the kind of day for being bossed about, so although I cleared the weeds away, I made myself a long cool drink and opted for the recliner. No hard chairs today.

'You're still breathing then?' began the challenge.

'Looks like it.' I sipped my drink and put it down in the shade. The recliner was inviting. I lay back and closed my eyes.

'Become aware of your breathing,' she almost whispered. 'Don't change it at first. Just listen to it. Become aware of its pattern. Relax into the pattern.' This was no challenge. I was used to this. I could do it very well thank you. She persisted, 'Once you feel comfortable with it, allow your breathing to deepen ... just a little and to slow down ... just a little. Feel good about that once you have achieved it. You will feel more deeply relaxed. And your attention will be focused on you. That's what you are aiming for.'

'What do I want to be focused on me for?' The spell was broken.

There was exasperation in her voice. She returned to being proactively Mother. 'Look dear, one of the main hassles with everyday life is that you are so busy dealing with what's going on around you, and doing what other people want you to, that you forget to listen to what you want and how you feel. Yes?' (It was almost a threat.) 'That's why you (the needle) got lost in the haystack of life. Before you can find a way out, you've got to find you. You have to find out what it feels like to be you again, and to discover what you really think. Focusing on your breathing is the first step.'

'Oh, I see,' I said, not really seeing at all.

'I told you before. It draws your attention to the inside of you rather than the outside.'

Realisation dawned, 'Oh, right!' I said.

'It's a good beginning. So, we'll start again now, shall we?' And we did.

I focused on my breathing and slowed it down. I deepened it little by little, until I found a comfortable rate.

'Don't try to push yourself beyond that. Aim for comfort,' said Sybil. I could swear she settled herself into the other chair and commandeered my drink. 'Today you will keep alert. You will be relaxed physically but alert mentally.'

I did my best, but before I could wonder what to be alert about, she said, 'Don't move! There's an insect on your leg.' I froze. 'Can you feel it?' I could feel it - light and feathery on my skin. 'Become aware of the feeling. It is part of you. Part of your sensitivity.' I didn't argue. I just felt. 'Now take that sensitivity and re-direct it to an incident that has upset you recently.' I did, and I was surprised to be aware of the intensity of feeling coursing through me.

Sheila at work had forgotten to include one of the new courses in an advert she'd placed in the local paper. When I objected, she criticised me for being so hooked on my own agenda I didn't notice when other people were struggling. I was angry first with her and then with me because she was right. I'd never noticed that before. And the anger was still coursing through me. I could feel my heart race and my stomach tighten.

'Now go back to that awkward situation and visualise it in detail.' I imagined the office with the sunshine coming in at an angle. I opened the door and strode straight up to her desk. I remembered her dark suit and the look in her eyes. I remembered my own words, my surprise at her directness and my attempt to make polite noises. 'Think about how you're feeling,' Sybil went on. 'Remember your thoughts and your actions at the time.' I recounted them to myself and found myself re-living a situation I thought I had dealt with. I was definitely still hurting. Definitely angry at the accusation of taking no-one else into consideration. Only too keen to wreak some revenge.

So began a Cook's Tour of my emotional self. Under Sybil's direction I became aware of a turbulent ocean which was me.

'I've been ignoring so much for so long,' I said out loud.

'That's because you've been paying attention to the outside world, not your inside world,' she said. 'You send yourself messages all the time, but most of the time you ignore them unless they become very loud indeed.'

'You mean like pain or illness?' I chipped in.

'Yes,' she said, 'or when you lose your temper.' I took her point. 'But if you paid attention before your symptoms shouted so loud, you'd be the better for it. You hide so much from yourself when really you should take a good long look at it instead. Ask yourself how you are feeling and take time to listen to the reply - just like you did just then.'

So my new regular exercise came in four stages. Stage One was to achieve relaxation. Stage Two was to focus my attention. Stage Three was to ask me how I was feeling. Stage Four was to listen to the answer.

'And if you want a real challenge,' Sybil added, 'have a go at re-writing the script.'

'How do I do that?' I asked from the comfort of my recliner.

'Go back to the original situation and think how you could change it for the better. You know the sort of thing. Could you have listened longer? Could you have noted the distress and sympathised? Could you have apologised? Live through the improved situation blow by blow and watch how your feelings change. That kind of thing,' she said, smiling sweetly. 'Think of it as another opportunity for self healing.'

My situation reviewed and reinforced, Sybil was brusque again. 'Right!' she said, 'Do that for a fortnight or so and let me know how things change. I'm off. I've things to do.'

There was something cold in my face. Wet and cold. It was Balthazar's nose. His brown eyes looked deeply into mine. His tail was wagging. It was tea time, and my glass was empty.

I remembered, as a child, watching a magician in a theatre act. And I recalled the intensity of watching him as I tried to work out how the tricks were done. I had forgotten that sort of intensity.

So many things lay claim to our attention that we're always taking information in from several things at once. The tv's on while we're listening to our children. The radio is playing as we drive along admiring the scenery. We're thinking one thing and saying another. I'd almost lost the art of focusing when Sybil presented me with her most recent exercise. As I rewound parts of my life and then pressed play, my mind was focused like a beam of light in a night sky. It was a good feeling and one that I wanted to apply to the outer life too.

I wanted to apply my mind to one thing at a time. It didn't matter whether it was the weekly shop, assembling a kitchen unit, understanding an editorial or facing up to the kind of person I was. If I made the effort, I thought, and applied the technique of focus to life, who knows how it might change?

I dared to imagine the liberated, new self!

CHAPTER 5

Late one sunny Sunday morning, I realised I still hadn't really got used to relishing doing nothing. Tom had already arranged to go fishing with George later on. I leafed through the local paper idly. A carboot sale was advertised - that would do. I reached for the phone.

'Mhairi? Laura. Are you doing anything this afternoon? There's a carboot on in Troon. Do you fancy it?' Mhairi worked for herself as an HR consultant, but ever since we were teenagers, jumble sales, second hand stalls and bargains had had their allure. You never really lose that spirit of questing for a treasure once it touches you.

'I'd love to, but if I don't get these tax forms sorted today, going to jail is the only thing I'll be doing,' she said mournfully. I commiserated with her over being self employed and resigned myself, with a sigh, to my own company.

'Well, I can see I've got your attention.' I was gazing mindlessly out of the window. Tom had left quarter of an hour ago and I was idly settling in to some time on my own. Sybil's voice drew my head together again. 'You're observing quite well. Let's take you a step further. It's music time. What goes on in your head when you sit back and listen to music?' She was almost conversational today. I started my answer warily in case she wasn't really looking for a response, but today she listened.

'Sometimes music conjures up memories, sometimes daydreams. I might find myself awash with colours, dancing on a beach or drifting through stars. On another day, I might be going over an event that happened earlier on, or worrying about something or sorting someone out. Sometimes I get so engrossed in what I'm thinking that I stop listening to the music altogether.'

'Ah, so you do pay attention to what's going on in there?' She tapped her head.

'Well, more so since you started dropping in,' I replied. 'Anyway, how should I be reacting to music?'

'How you react is not really important,' she said breezily. 'You being aware of how you react - now that is important! I've had you focusing your attention on your body and your emotions. Now you are going to focus a little more on your moods. You will learn to mood-watch, and the moods you will watch are yours! Are you ready?'

'As ready as I'll ever be.'

'Then choose yourself some music, and play!'

I chose a selection of classical music so that I could watch my reaction to the various different pieces. I put the CD on, put my feet up, closed my eyes and set to work. (Although it's hardly work to allow beautiful music wash around you and just "go with flow".) I watched myself as my emotions unfolded - sadness, exuberance, inspiration, melancholy, happiness. One feeling flowed into another, sparking off glimpses of times gone by, landscapes, dreamscapes, friends and memories. There was a theatre inside me and I was the director, artistic designer and company ... as well as the audience! There was so much more to me than I thought.

'Keep watching,' said Sybil. I opened my eyes as she broke my train of thought, but she didn't go away. 'It's your next exercise. You can keep doing the old ones whenever you feel like it, but for the next few weeks, make a regular time for listening to music and keep watching your reactions.'

'So this is to make me self conscious, is it?'

'No, no,' she said, running a discerning finger along my slightly dusty mantelpiece. 'Self conscious is the way you feel when you're the only one who turns up to a party in fancy dress. You're not learning to be self conscious, but you are learning to be conscious of your self, or self-aware, if you like. Watching yourself reacting to music is an easy way to begin the process.'

'What good will it do me?' I was thinking I might feel a bit guilty doing all this sitting around listening to music. The Work Ethic demanded some justification, although I could always say it was part of my attempt to slow down, I supposed.

'If you watch carefully as you use different kinds of music, you will begin to see how your mood can be manipulated by outside influences. It will also make you more sensitive to your moods. Once you become aware of what affects you, and how you are feeling, you can encourage yourself out of one mood and into another! How?' She'd guessed my question. 'By deciding which music to listen to, (or to recall) and choosing the music which brings you the mood you're looking for. That way you become in charge of your feelings instead of someone or something else.'

'By the way,' she added, 'you've got a visitor.' She vanished as the doorbell rang.

It was Mhairi. 'Do you still fancy that car boot sale?' she asked as the dogs flattened her by way of a welcome. I hauled them off her. 'Aren't you afraid of Income Tax Inspectors any more then?' She produced two dog biscuits from her enormous woolly cardigan and grinned wickedly. 'Living on the edge is what it's all about. Grab your bag and we'll make a quick getaway,' she said.

'OK. I could do with some new music,' I said, 'I'll explain as we go.' And bags in hand, we vanished too.

CHAPTER 6

In the weeks that followed, I realised that people could change my mood too. They broadcast their own sort of music. At work I could be feeling perfectly cheerful until Freda came for a moan. Specialising in why things went, would go or were going wrong, she was like music in a minor key and tinged my brightness with grey.

Bert was like music played too loud. His 'strident management style' gave no quarter. No-one got a word in edgeways. No-one was capable of a good idea, let alone an opinion. With all his aggression, I'd find myself folding in on myself with all my expansiveness disappearing fast. Sheila? Like folk songs, determinedly cheerful most of the time. But Jayne from Fine Arts had the effect of The Pearl Fishers - all beautiful and soothing, while Sam bowled along like a Forties musical with his good nature, restoring my equilibrium once again.

All these people in charge of my emotions! I could hardly believe it. But as I continued to 'Slow Down, Think Positive and Observe' I learned that it didn't have to be that way. That once I was aware of how I genuinely felt, I could maintain that feeling and reinforce it with my mood music. All I'd do was bring back to mind those powerful harmonies and melodies I'd chosen to listen to. It was a new kind of magic.

In the study, the word processor was all set up for typing up the minutes of the last team meeting. I gazed at the blank screen, wondering how to start.

'Forget the minutes.' It was Sybil again. 'I have an idea. Follow your inspiration and just type what comes to mind.'

'You mean you're not going to tell me how well I'm doing with all my self awareness?' I asked a touch peevishly.

'Of course not, you know that already. Type.' She really was too cheerful these days. Despite everything, I flexed my fingers and got started.

You are on holiday on a little island and you and your friends have decided to go for a walk. The sun is high and a gentle breeze dances among the long grass on the roadside verges. You are carrying a backpack and a jacket that you don't need. You want to be free of them. To your left is a simple farmhouse with a woman standing at the door. Your friends stop for a farmhouse tea, but you want to walk on for a while on your own. The farmer's wife offers to take your jacket and pack, suggesting you pick it up on your way back. You agree.

What a feeling of freedom as the weight is lifted from your shoulders!... Waving to your friends, you walk towards the wooden field gate with a lighter step and a feeling of anticipation.... You clamber over the gate, catching the tang of sea air as you do so, and jump down into a meadow of wild flowers... smell the scent of clover in the clear air!...

You follow a dusty track that wends its way through the meadow and gently up towards the hills... The sun is warm on your skin ... Feel it... You walk at your leisure, drifting past the buttercups and soft pink campion that dot the green of the grass... You feel part of this - at home in the landscape.

You hear the wheep of a seabird. Looking up, you are surprised at the intense blue of the cloudless sky.... you seem almost drawn up into it, but your feet take you further up the hill until you catch the first glimpse of the cove.... Standing on the hilltop, looking down, you see the grass on the far side gradually giving way to pale grey rock, soft beige sand and a tumble of rounded pebbles... Where the pebbles are, there too are larger rocks smoothed by ruthless winter seas and glinting now in bright sunlight... You travel towards them and find yourself at their side, dazzled now by white sunlight on a sapphire sea... Stand there, drinking in the light,... the freshness of the air.... the sound of the waves on the rocks ... It is good to be here.

Barefooted now, you stroll along the quiet shoreline, feeling the fine sand between your toes, the gentle breeze in your hair, the still-warm sun on your skin... Ahead is an old tree trunk, washed by the ocean and bleached white by the sun... Sit down on it now, letting it support you as you gaze out to sea, happily alone with your thoughts ... Take time to dwell on the scene. Take time to listen to your thoughts as the sea laps against the rocks...

Sitting there, it's almost as if the sea is washing away all strain, all anxiety... The warm breeze breathes new life into you... the far blue horizon whispers of hopes and dreams that could yet come true... it is a good place to be, a place to rest easy.

And yet, as time passes, you have a hankering to be with your friends once more. Refreshed now and no longer bare footed, you make your way happily past rocks and over pebbles, back to the grassy hilltop... You don't need to look back to the scene you have left because you know it will stay with you - a special place to visit in your mind when you need that special peace. On you go now, along the dusty track and through the clover meadow once again... Here is the wooden gate, and there is the farmhouse. Your friends are waiting for you, to welcome you back to their world again.

'Good,' said Sybil. 'That's about the measure of it. We are working quite well together.'

Looking at the sample of my creative writing, I couldn't help saying, 'What do you mean we are working well together?'

'You caught my drift quite well,' said Sybil unperturbed. 'How else can I get you to record the meditation? I could have talked you through it, but

19

you would never have remembered all the details.'

'You'll be telling me next it's telepathy.' I felt disgruntled now, but resolved to refuse to be disgruntled any longer. I would think sweetness and light at her instead.

'I don't need to,' she said smugly.

'Need to what?' I'd already lost the drift of this conversation.

'Tell you it's telepathy,' she said with what seemed like a smirk. Business-like, she continued, 'Now about this visualisation. I want you to make a tape of it. Read it out loud yourself, if you like, or if you've got a friend with a good voice, get them to do it for you. It's your next exercise you see. I want you to listen to it and allow yourself to make it real in every detail in your mind.'

She told me to listen to the visualisation with my eyes closed, and as I did so, to watch with my mind's eye the pictures that form as the description unfolds. It would be just like when I watched my own reaction to the different kinds of music. 'But this time, more definite ideas have been offered to you to encourage you to actively create the pictures in your mind,' she said. 'Some people call it a 'led meditation', but it's really just an excuse for your imagination to build pictures for you.'

I liked the sound of that.

'Are we moving away from self-awareness then?' (I decided that maybe we were working together after all.) Sybil smiled as if she'd won the contest and was now prepared to be gracious.

'For the moment, yes. We're going to tackle your mind's ability to visualise. You already started doing that in your music meditation, but now we're going to do it more thoroughly ... with a bit of discipline.'

'So what exactly am I supposed to be doing?'

She told me to start with the relaxation routine I'd learned earlier. After five minutes of that, I was to turn on the tape and 'go with it', visualising the details as I went along. 'Don't struggle with the details. If they come, fair enough. If they don't, expect them to come next time - there's no need to introduce stress into this. Just enjoy the process.' She suggested I do this regularly for a week or so, and note how the images and experiences changed as I progressed. I thought it would be worth having a go. 'You may come across professional relaxation tapes which help you to cope with stress. They would save you the bother of making up your own, but if you enjoyed this experience, you can make up some more of your own visualisations, or borrow some descriptions from literature. Work with a friend, if you like. Use a tape each time you have worked through your relaxation exercise together. It will add to the effect of relaxation, so you will both feel the benefit of them. Meanwhile, it will exercise your imagination, which is exactly what I want.'

Ever awkward, I had to ask, 'Why do you want to bring imagination into this?'

'Because you are learning how to communicate with yourself, and you communicate by using your imagination ... as you'll soon see.'

'Sybil, where do you go when you disappear on me?'

'Shopping.'

'Shopping?'

'For ideas. Must fly!' And that was it. End of audience.

Mhairi had been quite intrigued by my sudden interest in music, and once we'd finished gloating over our day's bargains, I told her something of Sybil's visits. The benefit of old friends is that they've watched you go through all sorts of crack-brained notions, so very little throws them after a while. Since then, I more or less kept her up to date with the news.

So it didn't take her long to volunteer to be the voice for the tape. It turned out she already had some relaxation tapes. We agreed to use them for variety, and swap notes on how we got on with our visualisations. It was good to have someone to talk it all through with.

CHAPTER 7

The more I worked with the visualisation tape, the more I realised that it came to life. On the first occasion, I just let the description unfold and went with it, noting the odd detail as I went along. As I became more familiar with it, I could hear the seabird's song and smell the salt air. The sand between my toes became tangible to me and the clear blue of the sky became startling and vibrant.

'It's almost as if we're feeding the tape with ourselves,' said Mhairi, 'and bringing it to life.' I thought I couldn't have put it better myself, until I remembered that 'I am incomparable' and there were supposed to be no more comparisons from now on.

We'd use other tapes from time to time, but working with the same one allowed us to watch the process and progress more easily.

Sybil left us to our own devices for two or three weeks.

I was getting ready to begin the relaxation exercise one evening, having left Tom to 'Newsnight' when she literally sprang to mind with, 'The next step is to keep your attention on what's going on inside your head.'

'But I thought that's what we were doing with the visualisation exercise,' I complained. I'd got sort of comfortable with it.

'Not at all!' said Sergeant Major. 'You've been listening to an external source commanding your imagination, and your imagination has been doing (more or less) what it's been told. Now we're going to exercise some willpower.' I wilted at the thought, but the pace was brisk.

'Some days this is easier to do than others! Today we're going to start with the outside world. Before you get settled to do your relaxation exercise, place something in front of you that is easy and interesting to look at. It could be a flower, or a photograph, an ornament or candle.' I looked around vacantly for something that would do. There was a pale blue scented candle on the study windowsill. That would do. I placed it in its holder on the occasional table to the side of my chair.

The Sergeant Major slipped into Therapist mode.

'Now take time to relax. Become aware of your breathing and once you are comfortable, open your eyes slowly and simply gaze at the object in front of you.' I did meekly as I was told. It didn't seem right. I'd forgotten to light the candle. Sybil maintained her therapeutic air while I felt foolish. We started again.

'Notice what it looks like. See where there is light and where there is shadow. Notice the contrast of colour, the shape, the size. Spend what seems like five minutes gazing gently at the object (don't distract yourself by consulting a watch or clock!). Then close your eyes and begin to re-create the object in your mind.'

'Easy as pie!' I thought.

'When you find that you have forgotten a detail or two, just open your eyes and gaze again,' she said ever so tolerantly, even although I never uttered a word. I took a quick squint. 'Then close them and begin the process once more until you have a clear picture in your mind.' I worked at this for a good five minutes.

'Sybil, this isn't as easy as it sounds. I just get one bit right and another detail escapes me. I can't hold the whole image at once.'

'You're trying too hard,' she said soothingly. I wasn't soothed. 'Do it daily. Practice this exercise regularly to help focus your mind on one item at a time. Keep using the same object. It will act as a sort of discipline which will be useful for you later.' As an afterthought, she added, 'I'll be back in a fortnight.'

My sense of timing was completely out. Newsnight was finished and Tom's head peeked around the door.

'You don't look very relaxed tonight, dear. What's the matter?'

'I'm a failure,' I said, blowing it out. 'Blame it on the candle.' He looked quizzically at me, and I realised it was my turn to be enigmatic.

'We're on to candles now,' I explained to Mhairi over a mug of coffee in her kitchen. 'You have to stare at them and then visualise them accurately in your mind's eye. It's driving me crazy. There's always a bit I can't get right.'

'Maybe you're trying too hard.'

'That's what Sybil said.' I looked at her suspiciously. But there was no sign of collusion, so I carried on. 'What made you say that?'

'The instructions for the visualisation exercise.' I looked blank. 'Don't you remember they said that if you didn't picture something in detail you were not to worry about it - just expect it to improve tomorrow? You should know, you told me!'

'Oh, yes,' I said weakly.

'There was no need to introduce stress into any of this, you said!' She was laughing now, and I couldn't blame her.

'Then I'll try not to try so hard,' I said, which is exactly what I did. And gradually it worked. I just let my attention sort of dwell on the candle and invited it to stay in my relaxed mind. The image started to become clearer. But I noticed that as soon as I became anxious about retaining it, it became harder and harder to hold.

'There has to be a lesson in there somewhere,' said Sybil out of the blue.

'I thought you weren't coming back for a fortnight,' I grumbled, sensing she was right.

'See you!' and with a wave she was gone again.

She was right, of course. I started to think about willpower. It wasn't really about being tensed up and determined. It had a lot more to do with being relaxed enough, composed enough, to know that you will win through in the end. 'Maybe you could win arguments just by being cool and sticking to the point,' I said to myself. 'I'll have to try that out sometime.'

By the end of the second week working away at holding the image of the candle, I was making progress. It had been a startling experience to discover that I wasn't as observant as I thought I was. I looked, but I didn't always see - if you see what I mean. I wondered if I was doing that with people and situations too. There was a lesson for me after all.

Just at that time, I was running a night class on Communication Skills. The women I was working with came from all walks of life. They were keen students who were there because they wanted to be. One student in particular struck me as pleasant and cheerful - a woman you would find it easy to approach because of her chatty style and pleasant manner.

When it came to "Delivering A Talk" she seemed to suffer a major change in personality. She became quiet and withdrawn. All her confidence disappeared. She panicked. Twice she approached me to ask to be let off with doing the assessment. On each occasion, I searched for what was the matter. I offered coping strategies, tips, ways round the difficult bits. Nothing worked. The more I tried to arm her with tools for survival, the worse the situation became. This student was awkward, time-consuming and stubborn, and I was endeavouring not to be exasperated.

It suddenly dawned on me that again I was trying too hard. I was so engrossed in finding ways to help, I wasn't 'seeing' the frightened woman in front of me. So I stopped trying. At the end of one evening session as the others were disappearing off, I created as calm an atmosphere as I could manage, perched on a desk, and asked, 'What made you like this?'

Out tumbled stories of a dominant father, a sarcastic school teacher, a husband un-nerved by her return to education, a personality driven to please everyone but herself. In short, she needed to be seen. She needed to be listened to. And for the first time I saw her as she was - not awkward, not demanding, just asking for help for herself. I needed to take time out from trying, and instead, to look and let someone else get a word in edgeways.

Once she'd told her story and I'd listened, she was able to face her challenge and deliver the talk. I didn't need to do anything else.

So, facing my own challenge, I learned to accept my unfocused state of mind and accept that progress would come gradually, if I expected it. Trying to rush it was a fool's game.

By the time I had burned my way through three or four candles, I was getting pretty good at holding the image in my mind. Mentally I felt more peaceful, more in control and (in a way) less driven. I became more inclined to let things happen in their own time.

'It's like growing a plant,' said the inevitable voice.

'What is?'

'Self awareness. No matter how much you try to make a plant grow and blossom, you will always achieve the best results when you allow it to unfold at its own pace and in its own time. The same is true with self awareness. When it is nurtured properly, your awareness will extend and grow in its own way and in its own time. It will not be as strong and clear if you try to force it.'

'Mhairi said she found it quite easy to hold an image in her mind,' I reported back. 'I took a lot longer.'

'Are we comparing again?' If Sybil ever wore half moon spectacles, she was looking over the top of them at me now.

'No. Not at all. Just reporting a fact,' I said, hanging on to my dignity.

'Then she is not a better or worse student than you are. She was just ready for the next exercise before you were. If you had tried to keep up with her, you would have undermined your own progress because you wouldn't have completed the last task fully or well. That would have made the next one less successful too. I'm glad you stuck to your guns,' she added, knowing full well that if I had known what the next exercise was, I'd have charged at it like a bull in a china shop weeks ago.

'Me too,' I said as sweetly as I could muster. 'What is the next exercise that I'm ready for anyway?'

'Abandon the candle.'

'What shall I look at instead?'

'Nothing.'

'What? Do you mean space?' I imagined staring cross-eyed into the fresh air in front of me.

'No, just close your eyes. Imagine a screen on the inside of your forehead. Imagine a light going on and then watch the images as they appear on the screen.'

'What images?'

'You'll soon see. You'll supply your own - they'll just come up on the screen. Oh, and keep a notepad with you. When you've sat for five minutes watching, note down what you see,' she said.

'Oh, will it be significant?' I asked, all ready to be intrigued.

'Not particularly,' she seemed a little off hand,' but it will encourage you to pay attention if you know you have to write something down afterwards.' There was a pause. 'If you get fed up with that, now and then, do the exercise with your friend Mhairi and take turns to tell each other what you saw after the watching time is over. That will motivate you both.'

'Sybil,' I said, 'you don't seem to be giving me your full attention.'

'Oh, am I not? I'm sorry. It's nearly finishing time.'

'Do you mean you have working hours and days off and that kind of thing?'

'Well, you don't expect me to work all the time, do you? Keep watching. You're doing fine!' And she was gone.

CHAPTER 8

Sometimes I feel as imaginative as a fried egg. The feeling comes over me most strongly as I stand in the middle of Tesco's wondering what to buy for next week's meals. It's too easy to fasten on to the railway track of what's usual and just keep going, week in - week out.

'You're not unimaginative,' sounded a voice as I chucked half a pound of pre-wrapped Cheddar into my trolley.

'Keep talking, that's just what I want to hear,' I thought to Sybil as I added a dozen free range eggs and some Lurpak. I was almost inspired to buy some vacuum packed snails just for the hell of it. I resisted. 'No imagination,' I thought again. I wheeled up and down the aisles on automatic pilot.

'Then what about all those pictures you've been watching on your inner screen?' Sybil retaliated. 'Where do you think they came from? Outer space?'

'Well, I suppose they were in my subconscious mind somewhere... the debris of a life observed,' I joked.

'And your imagination has nothing to do with your subconscious?' The question was left hanging in the air. 'Of course you've got imagination! It's working for you all the time. Mr Sheen.'

'Pardon?' I was gazing at boxes of soap powder.

'Mr Sheen. Polish. You've forgotten it. You'll notice I said you had an imagination - not a memory!' and with that, she left me to my shopping.

Now that I had a regular slot for my relaxation-cum-self awareness exercises, that was becoming something of a railway track too. A comfortable one and one that had positive side effects, but a habit just the same. Tom looked upon it as a harmless pastime, and as it didn't cost anything, it couldn't be bad. I was certainly more self aware, and I was wondering what would come next.

Right on cue, just as I'd settled myself down physically and was preparing to relax, Sybil bounced into my consciousness like a keep fit instructor. 'Right! We're going to call it meditation from now on, and get down to business.'

'Don't I need to sit cross-legged on special mats, burn joss sticks, ring bells and chant mantras?' That didn't seem to be me somehow. I knew I'd just been wondering if all this reflection wasn't getting a bit mundane but it didn't feel as if I'd achieved that level of imagination and creativity - not just yet, anyway.

Limbering up and breathing with intent, my Instructor delivered the following: 'Meditation is nothing fancy. Meditation is you watching you, being. Most of the time you don't quite achieve that, but you learn a lot from your mistakes. By now you're familiar with relaxing, steady breathing, watching your mind and concentrating. You're half way to meditation already. Let's take another step towards it. You know you can do it!'

'Without the bells, mats and mantras?'

'Of course!' There was a pause for effect. 'Tell me you have an active and fertile imagination.' I hesitated. 'Can't you see how imaginative your mind has been? Aren't you aware of the variety and detail of what you saw in your mind's eye? After all, you created all of that out of - well - nothing. Nothing but imagination. This lively imagination of yours is your greatest asset.' I couldn't get a word in. 'It pictures your thoughts for you, it allows you to visualise situations, it weaves your dreams and turns draft plans into reality. It's an asset.' I was vanquished. I believed her. 'And it's a liability.' There was a pause. I was devastated.

'When ?'

'When you want to be still. When you want to be at peace. When you need to be in tune with your inner self. Then that same imagination will tug at your attention like a demanding child. Then it is a liability.'

'Sybil, where are you taking me?' I bleated pathetically.

She beamed too broadly. 'But even demanding children teach us patience, tolerance, forbearance and love. You are about to learn that this 'picture maker' of yours can be your teacher. And you will learn it through meditation.'

'I think you're being a bit over dramatic here, Sybil. What do you really want me to do? In practical terms.'

'Dramatic? Last visit you complained I wasn't sufficiently focused on you. Now I'm over the top!' She tossed her blond curls, but nothing moved.

'I just think perhaps you're just trying too hard,' I said rather softly. There was a frisson in the silence.

'Touché! We shall proceed with a little more dignity,' and her tone changed. 'Now, to answer your question, I want you to tell yourself that you're not going to think any thoughts, you're just going to concentrate on being you. Aim to sit like that for five minutes.'

Five minutes seemed an excruciatingly long time. I felt I was nailing a lid on whatever produces thought, and the tighter I nailed it, the more pressure there was for the thoughts to express themselves. I even had a headache at the end of it.

'Well, what happened?'

'My head ached because I found it so hard not to think of something.'

'Then you are like most other people. You get settled down nicely, thinking of nothing, and then a thought appears. When you catch yourself thinking it, you get rid of the thought and start again. Yes?'

'Yes, but then another thought creeps in when I'm not looking and I have to get rid of that one too.'

'And then you find yourself getting quite bossy and insisting that there will be No More Thoughts. But of course, more come along. You might even have noticed that they come along more and more insistently until you feel you are fighting a losing battle.'

'It's hard to stop the production line. What's more, the harder I try, the busier my mind becomes.'

'Good! You worked really hard at that. Well done!'

I was bewildered again. 'So your idea of meditation is to try not to think of anything, and to fail?'

'No, no. The first step in meditation is to realise that your mind is constantly making pictures to distract you. You've just done that. That's why I'm so pleased with you.'

I blinked in reply, deciding in this situation that silence was golden.

'Now you're going to make a decision,' she said encouragingly.

'I am?' I wished I could look inscrutable instead of just plain dumb.

'You,' said Sybil pointing an imperious finger,' are going to decide not to be distracted by the distractions. Let your thoughts pass you by as if they belonged to someone else. The trick is not to declare war on them, because the more you try to repress them, the more energy you give them. Then they pop up again stronger than ever. So, instead of pressing them down, just watch them. Watch them as they pass over the screen of your mind. Don't be pleased with them. Don't be angry with them. Just watch them and expect them to go away in their own good time. They will. Try it.' She blew me a kiss - goodness knows why. 'See you in a couple of weeks!' and disappeared before I had time to respond.

Why I ever decided to strip our painted mantelpiece back to the natural wood, I'll never know. I think the classic excuse is, 'It seemed like a good idea at the time.' That was before I realised the ancient truth that under one layer of paint there are always at least another four, each more difficult to remove than the last, despite what the instructions on the paint remover can say. After the first two hours of hard slog, I reviewed my plans for the lounge and decided definitely not to strip the window frames, door and skirting as well. The mantelpiece would just be a unique focal point instead. I was sorely tempted just to cover my handiwork with a fresh coat of paint and forget the whole thing, but with all my new found mental discipline (sounds good, doesn't it?) I found myself determined to keep going and to put the thought into action. Besides, the whole project gave me plenty of time to practice this new meditation. Waiting for the chemical stripper to work, I realised that I didn't need to restrict meditation practice to a particular time or routine. Any space would do. Something like scraping paint didn't require my full attention, so I could request a still mind and watch the thoughts pass me by.

Gradually the pace of thoughts slowed a little. To my surprise, I found I was getting to know me better. That sounds a bit odd, but the exercise of watching made me seem like a character in a soap and I automatically starting putting the pieces of the 'character' together - like you do!

Recurring thoughts about things around the house that I hadn't yet done, began to tell me I was driving myself against another part of me that wanted to take her time. Why was I doing that? And things I thought didn't matter obviously did, because they kept popping up - the fact that I'd lost touch with an old university friend over the years. I found I was quite sad about that and knew that I could make more of an attempt to keep in touch if I wanted. In short, I realised I didn't listen to myself half the time, and I thought I might be a more contented person if I did.

I was learning more about me, but it wasn't all feel-good factor. I was shocked to find how intolerant I was (inside my head at least!) and how judgmental still, despite my motto of being incomparable. It was (sadly) as if it was now all right not to do me down, but it was still OK to do down everyone else. I began to feel distinctly uncomfortable with this kind of thing.

In an attempt to be righteous, I drew all my attention back to the exceedingly noxious surface of the mantelpiece, and succeeded in gouging it instead of stripping it. I flung the scraper on the floor. (So much for emotional awareness and control.)

'What's the matter with you?' Sybil popped her handbag on the coffee table and sat neatly in the fireside chair.

'It's this old varnish. It will simply not be removed and now I've scored it where everyone will see. I wish I'd never started!' I was definitely playing to the audience and was about to lean on the top of the mantelpiece for effect when I remembered it was still smothered in chemical stuff. The end result was arms flailing like windmills. I felt silly. Sybil discretely covered her smile behind a beautifully manicured hand. She composed herself. 'Try again.... What's the matter with you?' She was more serious this time.

I dropped down, deflated, and sat amid the sea of dust sheets. 'I don't like me very much.'

'But you're lovely...' she reached out to raise my face to hers.

'Don't patronise me, Sybil!' I snapped, turning my face away.

'... most of the time.' she added leaning back in her chair.

'I'm self centred, critical, hypercritical, vengeful. I think one thing and do another. I'm driven. I'm lazy. I'm a mess.'

'Apart from that you're OK.' she replied.

'Apart from that? There's not much left apart from that.' I was angry now. Angry with me, with the mantelpiece, with Sybil for not making it all better. I caught myself thinking that last thought. 'And pathetic!' I added for good measure.

She sat looking at me. Her hands were clasped in front of her, her index fingers together and touching her lips. Still she looked. Anger was a cloud around me.

'Then you're meditation's working,' she said very quietly. I shot her a lightning bolt of a look. 'Self awareness is not all love and light. There's darkness and despair to look at too. How can you claim to be aware when you only know the good bits?'

I went on looking, too choked up to say much. My throat was husky. 'It's too painful,' I whispered, looking down at my stained hands.

'Then don't do it.' It was like a jailer telling a prisoner she could go free.

CHAPTER 9

"With one bound Jack was free..." Or so the old fashioned adventure stories go.

I was free. I didn't need to look at me - of course I didn't. It was a waste of time and energy. Think of all the other things I could do instead. I got to my feet and phoned a friend or two; arranged a cinema visit and a spot of shopping. I turned on the radio, stuck the lid on the stripping solution, rolled up the dust sheets and went for a shower.

'What happened to the woodwork project?' queried Tom when he came home. 'Do you need a hand?'

'Not just now. I've decided new curtains would have more impact. I thought I'd just have a look round the fabric warehouse. Do you want to come?'

'I'll walk the dogs instead,' he said. 'That's more my forte. ...Is everything OK?'

'Of course it is. I'll see you later.'

The next few days were flurries of activity, but every time I passed the fireside chair I was aware of a sort of Residue-of-Sybil. She wasn't there, but she wasn't not there either. There was just a stare in the air. I refused to be this fanciful and decided to avoid the chair. 'Tom, do you fancy a weekend break?'

'What, now?'

'Yes. Why not?'

So we found a little hotel with good food, and walked over hills and through woodland. It was good, but not good enough to stop me thinking. Well, I'd already realised I couldn't stop thinking. What I mean was, it was good, but not good enough to wipe out the traces of my self-induced turmoil.

On our last afternoon walk, rain forced us to call a halt and go back to the hotel. Once dried and warmed up, we turned on the tv in our room to see what was on offer. A baddie in a black hat restrained the fragile heroine and thrust his revolver against her temple. 'One move and the Dame gets it,' he growled. The dialogue continued along inevitable lines.

'What realism! What significance! What drama!' said I, laying on the sarcasm.

'Only if you want to get that involved,' Tom replied, adding yet another spoonful of sugar to his coffee. 'Otherwise it's just a good story for a wet afternoon.' He took a sip, approved, and settled back against the pillows to watch the storyline unfold. Blood spurted from a mobster's eye. I shrieked and turned away towards Tom. He laughed, 'It's only a film. Just let it flow

31

past you!' and gave me a hug. I watched his enjoyment of the second rate movie. Then suddenly it dawned on me.

'You're right, you know,' I said.

'Of course I am.' Quite content, he continued watching the film while I snuggled in and fell asleep.

As we drove back home, I remembered first becoming aware of Sybil in the car that day in Edinburgh. Now the scenery rolled past us like the Technicolor backdrop to some epic or other. Tom was right - about the film, but about the meditation too. I had chosen to get so involved in all those passing thoughts that I had over-reacted to them. Sybil had said, 'Let your thoughts pass you by as if they belonged to someone else.' I hadn't been that objective, in fact I had literally become each one, with all the discomfort that caused. I should just have looked at them, recognised them and just let them go. I felt happier in myself.

'Did you ever decide what sort of curtains we were going to have in the lounge?' We were sitting at traffic lights at some roadworks.

'I've changed my mind again. I think the ones we have will do fine. Is your offer still open to help me with the mantelpiece?'

'Mm,' he smiled. 'I think the break did you some good.'

After our joint efforts, the next stage was sanding. That was left to me. With goggles and mask on, I looked like something out of a horror story. The dogs stayed well away. I, on the other hand, enjoyed myself, making plenty of noise and a good bit of progress. Things were shaping up.

In the middle of my self-made Sahara, I downed tools for a mug of tea to quench my thirst. Everything was shrouded in dust sheets again. This time I was in the fireside chair. 'I want to come back,' I thought to Sybil.

'What, back to prison?' her elbows were leaning on the top of my chair. I didn't need to look up.

'Back to doing as I'm told.' I gazed appreciatively at my smooth mantelpiece.

'You've got to expect a mess if you're going to strip back to perfection,' I mused. 'And sometimes you've got to accept a bit of help on the way.'

'Ah, you're a philosopher now, are you?' She raised her head a little and peered down her nose at our masterpiece.' You've got rid of the gouged bit then.'

'Tom restored it and I sanded it. It's looking good, isn't it?' I got up to blow some fine dust from the handiwork.

'Yes you are, I'm glad to say.' I didn't feel angry any more. 'You see, watching thinking is sometimes entertaining, sometimes uplifting, sometimes uncomfortable. Most people go through patches when they are displeased with or even ashamed of the thoughts that come to mind. You got upset when this happened to you. Work at not doing that. Remember, watch, wait, note and let go. A murky thought will occasionally arise from deep within you. Accept that you have a dark side - we all do. Look at it and then let go of it. It's a cleansing process. No-one expects you to clean up your act entirely all at one sitting. It's progress when you recognise there's some work to be done. Feel pleased that you've got that far. You know you'll tackle the difficulty as and when you can. That's much better than pretending the dark side doesn't exist, or putting the blame for it on to someone else. Watch, wait, note and let go. It's all part of getting to know yourself again. Enjoy making your own acquaintance: even the difficult stages.

Your meditation has begun now and will continue for the rest of your life. It's as natural as feeding or sleeping, and just as essential for health.'

'How do I work at the bits I don't like?'

'Think of it as restoration,' she smiled. 'Tackle one project at a time. Take as long as you need, and apply your new, improved idea to an area of your physical life.'

'Just like I did with the mantelpiece?'

'Yes, if you like. Just think ... metaphysical DIY!'

CHAPTER 10

There's no point in doing something unless it works. If there are no benefits attached, it's a waste of time as far as I'm concerned. The benefits don't need to be for me - just as long as someone is benefitting, that will do. So I kept on meditating as part of my daily routine because there were benefits. I even sat in the kitchen one day, and listed them.

mind clearer
more balanced point of view
less emotional
less anxious
more in control

'What's that?' said Mhairi, posting biscuits like letters down the dogs' throats.

'It's my benefits list,' I said, pushing it towards her and trying not to feel sheepish.

'I think you're right,' she said, pushing it back to me. 'That's the same sort of stuff we've been getting in a Stress Management thing at work.'

Suddenly I felt more confident about it all. If someone's paid to know all this, it must be right!

'So what else did they say it would do?' I ventured. She picked up another oatie biscuit and through the crumbs added, 'Oh, you will find you are more inventive and creative, happier and healthier. You will become more tolerant, more considerate, more likeable....' she brushed a fragment off her lips and continued, 'but perhaps that's the effects of more prolonged meditation!'

On such exchanges are the deepest of friendships built!

'Well, I didn't want to overwhelm you with too many changes at once,' I retaliated, getting up to make her an undeserved mug of coffee.

'I think this meditation stuff we've been doing lets the real you come through. It's like letting a tap run for a while,' she said. 'You get rid of all the luke-warm, yukky stuff and then the cool you flows.'

'Then here's to cool!' I said, toasting us in decaf. But what pleased me best was that by working away I had discovered for myself what the experts knew all along. It told me I was on the right lines, and that there was a point to this exploration of inner space. I was feeling pretty good.

'Eventually, you'll get it right,' said Sybil as I ploughed through the washing up a few hours later. I stared at the roasting tin looking for bits I'd missed.

'It looks clean to me,' I said turning it around critically.

'Your meditation,' she said, peering over my shoulder at the things I'd left to drip dry. I wondered if they'd pass muster. Apparently they did. 'There will come a time when you are engrossed in watching your thoughts and suddenly the next one won't come along. When you avoid becoming excited about your success here (remember, the whole aim of this meditation was to still your mind) you will continue just to 'be'. Even if this still moment only lasts a few seconds, you will find that mentally, physically and spiritually you will be refreshed.'

'Like my batteries were being recharged,' I polished off the roasting tin and put it aside as the dishwater gurgled its way down the drain.

'Don't struggle to hold on to the experience of this stillness,' Sybil went on, 'just accept the benefit it brings. With more experience you will slip more often into this state of 'being' and become happily familiar with it. You will have touched on the thinker behind the thoughts. The real you.'

'Once I've achieved those benefits, can I stop meditating?' I ventured blithely.

'Try it and see.'

'You mean they'll all start to unravel again, don't you?'

'Try it and see.' We were stuck on Replay, it seemed.

'I think I've tried it already,' I confessed, putting the cutlery away as I spoke. 'I've noticed that when I meditate I'm calm and sleep well. When I stop for more than a day or so, the niggles start up again.'

'Then you've answered your own question,' she said smugly. 'There is never an excuse to stop meditating. The aim is to understand the you of today. Each today is slightly different, so you are changing all the time too. As you change, you provide more material to learn from.'

'You said that once before. So there are by-products?'

'You're not an industrial process, you know.' The Schoolmistress had returned. 'But if you insist on being material, you were listing the by-products earlier today.' Madame Superior continued, 'I prefer to call them stages in your unfoldment myself : things like a still mind, knowing yourself, getting control of your emotions, choosing how you will react to life, changing yourself for the better, thinking more deeply, becoming more open to inspiration.'

I jotted down Sybil's spin-offs against my own benefits. 'Your list's longer than mine.'

'Quite.'

I ignored that and asked instead, 'So what's happening? Changes don't just come out of the blue, do they? There has to be a cause, otherwise they would happen to everyone like changes in the weather.' I sat down at the kitchen table with a household of brasses in front of me and began to polish away moronically. Sybil settled herself opposite me and leaned forward, her elbows on the table.

'Well, they do happen to everyone really, sooner or later.'

35

'But meditation encourages them to happen sooner rather than later?'

'Yes, I'd say so.' she pointed to a bit I'd missed on the base of a candlestick. I rubbed it dutifully.

'So does it work with the mind, or the personality or the spirit or what?'

'Mind, personality, spirit.... they're all labels. Don't get too hung up on them. They're labels stuck on the you that is the one in a billion.'

'Don't go all enigmatic on me, Sybil. Labels are useful for beginners like me. I need labels! Maybe once I understand better, I won't need them any more. And then I'll let them peel off and not replace them ... promise.'

'Well, maybe just for starters ...'

'Please.'

'OK.' She paused for a moment. 'How would you describe yourself?'

'I'm five foot seven, about nine and a half stone, grey-brown hair, greenish eyes. I have an expressive face and I talk a lot with my hands.'

'So you see yourself in purely physical terms?'

'No. There's more to me than that, I think. In fact, as I've grown older and my physical appearance has changed, I've never felt that the real me changed with it. I'm sort of inside it, if you see what I mean. Come to think of it, I could take up an exercise programme, have a facelift, dye my hair and so on. That might boost my confidence, but I don't think it would make me a different person. Well, I know I wouldn't be a different person.'

'So how would you describe yourself?' she persisted.

'I've worked professionally in education all my life. I'm communicative. I think I'm quite creative. I'm thoughtful ... but I'm also a bit of a softie, I'm a sucker for a sob story. It's important that I'm loved and that I have people around me to love. Sometimes if I think something is wrong, I surprise myself by standing up for people and causes.' I tailed off a bit after that, realising that it was a challenge not to describe myself in physical terms.

'You are telling me you are what you do,' said Sybil with a tinge of a challenge in her voice.

'No. I do what I do because I'm the way I am.'

'So what way are you?'

'I am the watcher in my meditation. I am the feeler of my emotions. I am the thinker of my thoughts.' I could feel being stretched, or stretching out to reach for something else. 'I'm not you!' I concluded with a splutter.

'How do you know?' The corners of her eyes crinkled.

'Because I can't see me from where you are sitting!' was the first answer that came into my head. Sybil laughed.

'Then are you a point of view, a perceiver?'

'Yes, in a way, I suppose I am.'

'What happens when you are asleep, or you're not perceiving? Do you

36

cease to exist?'

'No, of course not.' I could feel the effort of drawing my thoughts together. 'Just because I'm not active doesn't mean I cease to exist. I am in a passive state when I'm not active. Sometimes I perceive, sometimes I reflect on what I see. At other times I react or don't react. At those times, like you say, I just am.'

'Just am what?' She wasn't going to give up. Neither was I.

'Just am run out of metal polish!' I declared obstinately.

One delicate eyebrow was raised slightly. 'Try again.'

'Just am alive! That's my last offer Sybil. You've got me beat.'

CHAPTER 11

Surveying the array of shining brasses before me, I felt satisfied with at least one part of the evening's work. My hands, grey-green from the metal polish were evidence of all the effort I'd put in.

'That's pretty good.' Sybil didn't seem as teed off as I thought she'd be. 'You are an expression of the life force, are you?'

'That'll do me.' I was beginning to flag now, and had little left to argue with. 'Just like these polished brasses are an expression of my physical force ... or whatever.'

'Only there's a difference, isn't there?' she said. 'Between you and the brasses.'

'I'm conscious and they're not.'

'Right. Don't give up when you're winning!' she said, propping up her chin with one hand, elbows still on the table. 'Now answer me another question.'

I grimaced. 'How is your conscious expression of the life force different from everyone else's?'

I pushed my fingers over my face and through my hair in an attempt to think more clearly. Then suddenly stopped with a notion that I probably looked like a frightened zebra with pale grey stripes from my polish-covered fingers. Why worry? I thought, I am not my body anyway, and continued. 'Maybe because life is forced into certain ways of expression through the circumstances prevailing at the time.'

'Go on,' she encouraged.

I had a sudden flash of inspiration. 'Well, imagine that the life force is water and the prevailing circumstances affecting it are the watering can. All the life force flows steadily along the spout until it reaches that perforated rose thing on the end of it.'

'How delicately you put things!'

'Well, at that point some of the force is expressed at a high level, some at a lower, some to the right, some to the left, and so on. Each little stream of water has its own distinct place and curve. So each one is different because of the circumstances, but each is made of the same stuff. ... How about that?' I was quite delighted with myself, and then quite embarrassed at being so delighted. Sybil watched my confusion for a moment.

'That'll do nicely,' she said. 'We'll leave it there for now.'

I'd just got my second wind, 'But Sybil, what happened to your explanation of meditation? You've hardly said a word. Don't I get my explanation?'

'You of all people ought to know better than that,' she said, getting up and stretching. 'If I do nothing but deliver answers to you, you'll never learn anything. Education's not about hammering information into the student as you well know. It's about leading the student towards an understanding of her own making. I think I'm leading you on very well,' she added and disappeared into the twilight. Leaving me to ponder whether 'leading you on' was a good thing or not.

Marjorie was an old neighbour of mine. She'd been widowed for about five years, so when she'd to go to the local hospital for some tests, I was happy to take her along and sit with her until she'd seen the consultant. She'd been having some dizzy turns and her stomach was permanently upset, so her doctor had referred her for a few tests and a scan. Sitting in the waiting area, we could watch the world go by as patients and visitors trundled along a main corridor to one side of us. We knew it could be a long wait and had come armed with magazines and boxes of juice.

Marjorie fidgeted a little between our sporadic bursts of chit-chat. Despite my best efforts she waited nervously to be called. Tense and alert like a little dog listening for her master's voice.

'Mrs Norden?' It rang out at last. I patted her hand and said I'd wait. She aimed for the pink door everyone else had passed through. Gazing after her, I wondered what she had been like as a young woman - a woman I would never know. However much she told me about her past, I would always see the younger Marjorie through the lens of Marjorie Today.

A portly woman of about fifty flapped along the main corridor. She was laden with poly bags and her winter coat seemed too heavy for her. A five-year old girl skipped along beside her, delighted with the bunch of artificial flowers she was holding. 'Jenny, watch your feet on the slippy floor,' the woman warned, puffing as she went. It was like looking at a picture of past and present, I mused. What happened to change a carefree, pretty girl to into an overheated, harassed woman?

Then again a skinny teenager strode by in impossibly high trainers. I could hear the music from his walkman from where I was sitting and see the designer logo on his sweatshirt. His parents probably never dreamt of the lifestyle he had today. It wasn't even vaguely possible when they were teenagers ... no CDs, no internet, satellite tv or mobile phones - and a completely different set of expectations.

Musing the time away, I realised that I wouldn't be me if I was born today rather than nearly fifty years ago. Not even if I was born to the same parents in the same place. The culture was so different, the history was different, even the physical environment was different. I'd lived through national strikes, not drug misuse - so social problems were different too. I'd never needed to look for a job: there were plenty to choose from. All these things shaped me, helped me to grow into what I am right now. I realised with some amusement that I could have turned out differently! That despite my genes, any one of a million incidents or influences could have shaped me into something different.

'I am an experiment.' I thought. 'There's never been one of me before; there's only one exactly like me just now; and there'll only ever be one of me in the future!'

'You mean, you're one in a billion?'

Along the corridor, I heard the swish of the automatic doors closing and only just caught a glimpse of a brightly coloured wrap disappearing behind them. Sybil was nowhere to be seen.

'I'm back dear,' Marjorie was leaning over me to break my gaze. She took me by surprise. 'It wasn't as bad as I thought,' she smiled and sat down beside me. 'They gave me an anaesthetic before they put the tube thing in my throat, so I didn't know a thing. And then they gave me a sandwich when I came round. That was a surprise. I didn't know they did that. Egg and cress, very nice - and a cup of tea to follow.' I was glad to see her tension was all gone. A weight was off her shoulders and the results would be two or three weeks away. 'Shall we go now?' she said cheerfully, so we did.

CHAPTER 12

I don't know what drew me to the little water-colour originally, but we bought it not long after we were married, and it has hung in my study ever since. It's a picture of a red-haired, bearded wizard who looks like a refugee from the late sixties.

With thonged leather sandals tied to his large pale feet, he wears a tie-dyed kaftan with a baggy pocket and wide sleeves. The colours work their way round the spotted fabric - lemon, orange, pale green, turquoise, blue and purple. On his stooped back he carries a sort of cotton knapsack, and on his head is a watery blue pointed hat with white moon and stars. His wild red hair bushes out from beneath it.

There is only a hint of a mountainous landscape around him. From his bearded face you can see he is oblivious to it all. His eyes are closed tight in concentration. Delicately poised in his right hand is a wand like a conductor's baton. He is waving it over his outstretched left hand on which a frog is perched. The frog's look of resignation contrasts with the smug pleasure on the face of the grey cat winding its way round the ankles of the transfixed magician.

Maybe I like it because of its uncertainty. I can never make up my mind whether this wizard has just transformed something into the frog, or whether he is just about to transform the frog into something else. If it's the latter, by the look on the cat's face, I wouldn't be surprised if the spell didn't work. But you never know .... I wonder if the wizard will get a shock when he opens his eyes.

His eyes are hazel, I've decided, because you wouldn't expect that with red hair. Over years in his company, I divined his name's Magnus and he's on a spiritual quest (he doesn't look the practical type). He has to be Scottish because no self-respecting Scotsman would be seen dead in a kaftan like that. The cat is Irish with the gift of the gab and is called Opus. The frog's - well - just the frog.

One evening, my attention wandered towards him. 'Here is the story so far,' Magnus said. 'You're not just an experiment, you're an on-going experiment of transformation.'

'In fact, you'll never be completed,' chipped in Opus from behind the kaftan. 'You'll just go on and on and ...'

'That'll do!' interrupted his master, as he turned more fully towards me. 'You see, I want to tell you a story.' I settled down obligingly.

'Deep in the mists of time, in a land far away,' he started, 'there lived a magician. But the mists were so swirling and thick and deep, that the magician (who was manfully ploughing through them at the time) forgot what he was supposed to be doing. 'I must seek far and wide,' he said to himself, 'and then surely I shall stumble across it some day and remember what I was doing in the first place.' So he set off upon his journey of discovery. Over oceans of experience he sailed towards unexplored continents. Unfortunately, however, at a shallower point in the mists of time, his ship was wrecked in a tempest and he found himself cast up on a strange island.

His wizard's robes had magically saved him from the biting cold of the water, but he was well and truly soaked through. Slowly, against the weight of all that water, he struggled to his feet.

'Oi! Who are you?' shouted an unwelcoming voice. The magician looked up and surveyed a dark, bleak and rugged landscape. 'Haw Jimmy!' said the voice, answering its own question, 'What are you doing here?' This time the magician spotted a crow perched on some black rocks nearby.

'I don't know,' said the magician, still a bit shaken from his experience.

'This is no place for the likes of you,' said the crow insistently. 'There's nothing here, and it rains all the time. You'd better go.'

'What did you say it was called?' said the magician, running his eye over the skyline.

'This,' said the crow, with doom in his voice, 'is the Isle of Barren. You won't last five minutes here.'

'I don't know,' said the old man ringing the sea water out of his robes. 'It's OK. It's got potential.' The drops of water landed on the rocks and trickled into the cracks there.

'Aye, that'll be right!' coughed the crow, and off he flew, never noticing the sea pinks beginning to grow in the cracks in the rocks, or the tall sea grasses which stirred in the places where the old man had passed.

The magician watched the direction the bird flew in and chose the opposite one for himself. He would follow the shoreline and see where it took him. In the days and nights that passed, he wended his way inland away from the shore, and every time the rain stopped (because the crow was right - it did rain a lot) the magician would pause awhile to wring out his robes and gaze around him. On this occasion, there was a splash and then a flapping beside him.

'You're still here then,' said the crow. 'There's not much point in staying, you know. There's nothing here but gloom, and wet gloom at that.'

'I don't know, it's got potential,' said the visitor catching a rare glimpse of sunshine. 'It's not all bad.'

'Aye, like the plague's not all bad!' and as an afterthought, 'You're weird, do you know that?' The crow flapped off, never noticing the fresh grass at his feet or the little shrubs tucked in against the hillside out of the wind. But there was a sweeter smell in the air, he thought.

42

Time slipped by like the pale sand lifted by the breeze on a brighter day. The crow watched his distant companion journey around the island, meandering slowly upwards towards its central peak. Regularly the magician wrung the rain from his robes and continued on his way. Regularly the crow accosted him with his miserable comments and regularly the reply came back, 'I don't know, it's got potential.' The bird got used to this comfortable repartee and to the sudden appearance of a tree here and some ferns there, primroses in the spring and bracken in the summer.

One summer evening he spied the magician at the top of the mountain. The air was still and clear and the magician was seated on a boulder, leaning back on the rock. It was a grand view. Little streams tumbled down through ferny gorges, past lush grass and bushy hawthorn. The scent of heather was in the air and as the eye followed the contours of the island to the pale gold shoreline, the fine silver waves edged a blue sea. It was good.

'Haw Jimmy!' the crow startled him. 'Why did you come here? I never thought you'd last, you know.'

'I came to find something,' said the magician, staring into space.

'What? '

'Me, I think.'

'Oh yes?' huffed the crow. 'And where might you be?'

'Here,' said the magician, rising with both arms spread wide. 'Every drop of rain transformed! That's me!' He gave a little laugh of excitement and began to twirl.

'Don't you think you're getting a bit emotional here?' said the crow fidgeting from one foot to the other.

'I wondered who I was,' the magician's dance quickened, 'and then I let life pour through me, and look what I made of it! This is me!' he shouted at the beautiful island. 'This is me!' as the last few drops fell from his hem.

'Well, I don't know,' said the crow, peering about him. 'It's ...' he turned to his companion who was nowhere to be seen. Gone. Vanished. But he didn't have time to be surprised. As he turned, he caught a glimpse of soft grey around his shoulders and dazzling white on his chest. He shook a foot out to confirm his fears. Yes. It was orange!

A crow no more, the bird took to the air in fright, wondering what to do with himself and his new image. High and higher he soared, hoping the night would return its colour to him. But in another dawn he heard a cry, cries, and flew towards their source. Far below, tossed on heavy seas, a ship and its crew were in difficulties. The grey and white bird dipped and dived, to land adeptly on the masthead.

'Are we close to land?' shouted one of the frightened seamen.

'Not far,' said the bird, 'follow me!' and he flew in the direction of his

43

island. As the sea calmed, the little boat reset its course and finally dropped anchor in sight of the island. The crew clambered into the lifeboat as the gull wheeled above them. Before long, they set foot on the shore.

'What do you call this place?' shouted the ship's master to his feathered guide.

'It's the Isle of Barren' called the bird from a bluer sky.

'The Isle of Arran?' said the master. 'Well, it's beautiful!'

'It's OK,' said the bird, 'it's got potential.'

There was laughter in a land beyond the mists of time, for the magician's work was complete.

'I've been to Arran,' I said. 'It's not far from here. And you're right - it does rain there a lot and it is beautiful.'

'That,' said Magnus, 'is NOT the point.'

'The point is, you've upset him,' purred Opus superciliously.

'That is NOT the point ....' muttered Magnus, striding back into his picture.

CHAPTER 13

'You're not the magician, you know,' said Sybil as I stirred thoughtfully at the strawberries bubbling away in the pan. '...Even if you do have the cauldron.' I kept on stirring and waited for the next bit. There always was a next bit. She leaned over the jam pan and sniffed at the steamy aroma.

'Mm,' she went. Apparently I was supposed to respond.

'Well, I did think I might be. After all, you said his task was transformation didn't you? Taking life and making the most of it? Isn't that what you are encouraging me to do by slowing down, observing and reacting?'

'That's only part of the story,' she said, propped against the worktop and watching the bubbles as I skimmed off the froth. 'You're the crow too.'

'Thanks very much,' I said, 'that's all I need.'

'And the island as well,' she added as if that would make me feel better.

'How come?' I continued to stir gloomily.

'You are working at transforming the life that flows through you into something worth while.'

'So that's the island landscape,' I butted in.

'But you are hoping to transform yourself too, and evidence of that change comes in outward things like the way you express yourself, your attitudes and your actions.'

'Which is the crow..... so don't I get to be the magician too?'

'Of course you do! He takes all life throws at him,'

'Mostly rain.'

'processes it and wrings out the product.... his own particular magic.' There was a pause. 'What did you think the meditation and the observing was all about?'

'Self awareness, like you said.'

'Exactly. Unless you are aware of you, who you are and what you think, you'll never make the most of your life. Awareness, consciousness ... that's what it's all about. You're expanding your consciousness.' She added this last part meaningfully, as if communicating with the retarded, which was ironic under the circumstances.

'I thought that's what drugs did,' I said, testing some jam on a cold saucer. It wrinkled. Time to get the warmed jars out of the oven.

'Well some do,' said Sybil, 'but they skip steps in the process of unfolding and do a lot of damage.'

'What do you mean 'steps in the process', I thought consciousness just happened,' I said, watching the hot crimson jam slither off the ladle and into a jar.

'Did that jam just happen?' she said, nodding towards the jars.

'No. You know it didn't. It started as raw fruit. It was washed and hulled and weighed. The sugar was weighed out proportionately, lemon juice added. It was heated and brought to the boil, then simmered and skimmed until it was ready to set .... and then it was jam.'

'But what if you skipped a step or two, or simmered it for half the time because you were desperate to taste the jam ... what then?'

'You might have something that tasted nice, but it wouldn't be jam and it wouldn't keep. It would soon go off.'

'How do you know that?'

'Two reasons, I suppose,' I said, filling the last jar with a sense of satisfaction. 'One - my Mum taught me how to make jam properly as I suppose her mother taught her, and part of the instructions were to follow the instructions! It was all explained what would go wrong if you tried to take short cuts. Two - having taken the short cuts, I learned from experience and so now I know why the instructions are there in the first place.'

'Ah, so you're doubly wise!'

'Don't you believe it!' I steeped the pan and set about wiping the occasional sticky patch off the shiny glass jars.

'Well, the same is true of expanding consciousness. The received wisdom, handed down through the ages, is that it is a process of growth and each of the stages has to be arrived at, experienced and understood in a standard order before you have the ability or capacity to move on to the next. Those who try to skip a stage - like the apprentice jam maker you once were - may taste the experience of stages further along the way, but the taste is fleeting. It doesn't last. It simply creates the longing for another and another and another experience, each one less satisfying than the previous one. You become soul sick. Then physical addiction sets in and the wider consciousness you were too keen to experience becomes more and more limited, more degraded, less competent, until your whole being weakens and almost dwindles away. Unless it's caught in time. You may not think it, but impatience can be fatal.'

I finished drying the old brass jam pan and laid it to one side.

'There's a season for making jam,' Sybil said more cheerfully, 'and there's an appropriate time in each person's life for their consciousness to develop. You've reached one of those stages now. You've made a home and a career, established yourself as an individual, and now you've time to reflect. Time to listen not to the voices from outside yourself, but to the voices on the inside. Time to look beyond the material and the emotional, and even the intellectual. You've time to look from different points of view. To see yourself and life more clearly.'

'You mean 'Life Can Only Be Understood Backwards'.' I said, quoting from a poster I once saw.

'I told you you were the magician too!' she exclaimed. 'That's why he only knew who he was when he looked back over his journey.'

I think I'd just been given a gold star.

46

CHAPTER 14

I could see the dogs staring dolefully at me in the rear view mirror. 'Traitor!' both pairs of eyes were saying to me. We were returning from the vet's where I'd betrayed them into getting their vaccination boosters at extraordinary expense. Then I'd added insult to injury by abandoning them in a supermarket car park while I went to purchase the return of their affections by way of two maxi hide chews. My status in their eyes was still uncertain by the time we arrived home in the pouring rain.

As I pulled on the handbrake I wondered how Marjorie was doing. It was good to be home. I opened the hatchback and watched the dogs make their leap for freedom. With bags of goodies in one hand and the front door key in the other, I was suddenly almost acceptable again. Their tails waved expectantly as noses snuffled the bag. We tumbled into the hallway. The carrier was demolished and happiness restored.

Well, theirs was, but I still felt uneasy. Part of me wanted to put my feet up, but another part had already picked up the scissors in the kitchen and was making her way out to the back garden. I'd just take her a few flowers - some marigolds, a few daisies, a rose or two and maybe some of that blue stuff. Just a posy.

Soon I was at Marjorie's kitchen door, flowers in hand. Through the rain-spotted glass I could see her seated with her back to me. I tapped on the window. She jumped, taken by surprise. 'Oh, I'm so glad you came!' she said, ignoring the flowers. She was trying to brush away the tears in her eyes. I led her back to the kitchen table and sat down beside her, trying to read her face. 'I've to go into hospital and I don't know where to begin.'

'You've had the result of the scan, haven't you?' It was more of a statement than a question.

As the tears ran freely, she sobbed into my shoulder. My arms circled round her, a poor defence against her fears. Over the inevitable cup of tea, the day arranged itself. The doctor had already booked her in after this morning's appointment. We cancelled the ambulance he had arranged for her and together we packed the frail necessities - a couple of nighties, dressing gown, toiletries, comb, hankies, a magazine, a few boiled sweets, slippers, maybe a clock - who knows. I brought the car round for her. Checked the windows and doors were locked, and we were away.

As she sat vulnerable in her chair by the bed, giving the hospital registrar her details, I remembered the flowers abandoned on her kitchen table. A nurse came with a plastic bracelet with her name on. 'I'll be in at seven tonight,' I whispered at my friend, giving her a peck on the cheek, but already she was in another world. I turned on my heel and told myself she was going to be all right.

Now her loss of weight, her tiredness, the queasiness and the dizzy turns fitted into a picture I didn't want to see. But I was looking at it now, in the car park, grateful that it was still raining to camouflage my tears.

I opened the car door and slipped inside as if its protection from the rain would protect me from my own emotion. I turned the radio on and the de-mister. 'I shouldn't be this certain,' I cried out to Sybil, 'but I know she's going to die.'

She was so gentle, sitting there beside me. No banter. No cleverness. 'Then help her,' she said softly.

The rain drizzled down the windscreen. 'How can I help her?' It seemed my throat was cracking.

'Be with her. Listen to her. Keep her company. Soothe her. Do what you feel, not just what you know.'

'I feel so much I don't know what I feel,' I said, brushing my own tears away now.

'Take some time.' Sybil was almost hypnotic. 'Go home. Sit awhile. Do something gentle. Then you'll know how you feel. Then you'll feel better.'

I didn't see Sybil touch me but I could feel her gentleness seep into my turmoil, turning the hot red of my feeling into something pastel like pink and lavender at dusk. I felt steadier, calmer. I turned on the ignition and drove the journey home.

There was a message on the ansaphone from Iris, Marjorie's daughter. I phoned her back to assure her her mother was safely installed in the hospital and that Tom and I would visit her that night.

'They've just settled her in,' I said, ' so there have been no extra tests yet. There's nothing much to report.' Iris said she'd be up from Manchester tomorrow and I promised to get a few things in for her as she'd be staying at her Mum's for a few days at least.

It felt better to be busy, to have things to do. Tom and I had a rushed meal and went back to the hospital for visiting time. She was sleeping when we arrived, so we sat quietly with her, feeling it would be a shame to disturb her. I held her hand softly and found myself mentally enveloping her in a cover of love, reassurance, gentleness. Her blue eyes flickered open and gazed a little past us. She smiled a little and said, 'I'm fine.' Then her eyes closed again and she dozed off.

At the end of visiting time, we asked the nurse in charge to let Marjorie know her daughter would be with her tomorrow, and that we had been for a visit. We left some fruit on top of her cabinet and took our leave.

'You can only be there, can't you?' I said to Tom as we walked along the panelled corridor of the hospital.

'There's nothing much else you can do,' he replied. 'Not at this stage. You just have to let the medics do their stuff.' We walked silently back to the car, happy to have each other's company, and perhaps more aware than usual of the value of that companionship.

It had been a long day, but later that evening I went up to the study to see if I was up to meditation. I expected my mind to be all over the place and wasn't expecting much in the way of serenity, but I was surprised. Perhaps my physical tiredness made it easier than usual to relax and just accept the impressions that came to me. It was as if I didn't want to join in - I just wanted to watch, or to allow the passive experience to happen.

Deeper and deeper was the inner silence I floated in. I seemed to dissolve in it, to have no shape or form. I extended in all directions yet felt the depth and profundity of me - if that makes any sense. And from somewhere within this depth, a soft light seemed to emerge. At first it simply tinged the edges of the darkness that was me. Then it began to filter through it. Gradually the darkness paled and lightened. A rush of emotion welled up within me and tears slowly trickled from my eyes. There was no sobbing, no sound. Lighter still I became and then brighter. I could feel the intensity of the energy build. No longer just a light, it was a force that continued to build. It became a power, a strength that grew beyond me, radiating through me.

I have never felt so still and so active at one and the same time. Never felt so completely and individually myself while at the same time experiencing what I can only call the Beyond-Myself. I sat, in awe and wonder at it all.

I cannot say how long I sat like that, for I don't know when the experience began, to measure it against the time when I opened my eyes. I looked around me, like a child fresh out of a dream, feeling surprised at the familiar objects about me. And then oh so disappointed that I had broken the experience and that it was gone. The experience moved like a liner upon an ocean, leaving me in my little boat, to feel the tug and swell of the wash behind it.

'Use the healing light, use the healing light,' echoed in my brain. 'Use the healing light.'

CHAPTER 15

'You're looking distracted,' said Mhairi over a cup of coffee in the kitchen. She'd come over to hear how Marjorie was and see if there was anything she could do. I'd already told her about the tests and their results, how Iris had arrived and how more tests had been done, medication changed and how Marjorie's good days and bad days had become good and bad moments as her moods swung and her hopes rose and fell. 'So what are you thinking?'

'Do you believe in healing?' I asked, point blank.

'Do I believe people get better? Yes, of course I do,' she paused, 'but that's not what you're asking, is it?'

'No. I'm not sure what I do mean.' I stopped to think. 'Do you think someone can cause another person to get better by ...' I was groping for the right words, 'by willing them to?'

'Like praying for them, you mean?'

'Well, I hadn't thought about it like praying, but yes, I suppose so. Praying is like focusing your attention on something ..... in a way.'

'All kinds of churches pray for the sick,' said Mhairi looking at me strangely. 'They talk about healing the sick, faith healing, that sort of thing. Are you thinking of asking a priest or someone to help Marjorie?'

'Well, maybe that's a good idea. I hadn't thought of that - I'll see what Iris thinks.' I petered out.

'Spill the beans!' said Mhairi. 'Has Sybil been at you again?'

'I wish I knew! I sensed her the day I took Marjorie to hospital. I was really upset, you know? I suppose I panicked and thought she was going to die. Sybil calmed me down, told me to sit a while and do something gentle, said then I'd know how I felt and that then I'd cope.'

'And?'

'And so after Tom and I came back from the hospital that first night, I went to meditate. You know, to try and do something normal and routine.'

'Except it wasn't normal and routine,' she prompted.

'No. I've never felt anything like it.' An echo of its emotion came back to me. But I hung on to my coffee mug and made a determined effort to explain, or at least describe, it all to Mhairi.

'So, assuming that the healing light was the light I experienced,' I said, putting down my empty mug, 'how do I use it?'

'What have you tried so far?'

'Nothing. I'm genuinely clueless. I don't know where to start.' I laughed. 'That's why I'm asking you. I thought you might have read something in a book, or been to a seminar somewhere ....' Just occasionally I would tease

50

her about her 'alternative' interests.

'You don't need to ask me,' she said, 'you're not nearly so clueless as you think. We've been doing self-healing in meditation for ages. You taught me!' she added. 'Just direct your thought to Marjorie. Wrap her up in that light you were feeling. Imagine her inside it feeling as good as you did.'

'Do you think it would work? I never thought of that - it's so obvious. Do you think it might work?'

'Me? I haven't a clue. But the self healing helped you, and I feel the benefit from my practice. It has to be worth trying.' I thought about it in silence. 'It can't do any harm.'

'And it might do some good. It just might.' I could feel a tingle of excitement.

'I'll do it too if you think that's allowed,' said Mhairi, 'and we'll watch for results.'

We agreed to 'send' at 10.30pm for the next week and see what happened.

Iris was beginning to show the strain. She had left her two children with her mother-in-law in Manchester and really wanted to be in two places at once. The uncertainty about her mum's condition meant that it was impossible to make plans. The previous weekend, her husband Peter and the kids had come up to see her and gran, but Sunday evening they returned home and left her feeling forlorn. We took it in turn to visit and report back on results and progress.

Now it was Friday - the end of her second week in hospital - and we knew the brain scan had picked up a shadow. The specialist had identified an area where there had been some bleeding. If all went well, he said, there would be no need to operate. The whole thing could settle back down again. We dared to hope, and we had good reason. It was nearing the end of Mhairi's and my 'sending'. Marjorie was still frail looking, but she was sleeping less and her mood was more often tranquil and cheerful than not.

Iris remarked on the change. 'Do you think it might be due to her medication?' I asked, not sure enough of my 'sending' to talk about it with her.

'No. I thought that as well, so I asked her nurse about it. I'm really surprised,' she said, 'Nurse said she was on very little medication, just something to help her sleep at night. They seem to think that in this case, Nature is the best healer, and they're letting it take its course.'

I was quietly satisfied. I phoned Mhairi with the results and the message: 'Keep sending!'

Two days later, a rather bewildered Iris popped in. 'They're sending her home tomorrow,' she said. By the look on her face, I don't think she knew whether to be happy or sad.

'They said she was making good progress and because I'm here to look after her, that with supervision she'd be fine. The doctor will call in to see her in the afternoon.'

I shared her excitement and uncertainty. Her progress had been recognised.

With the warm autumn sunlight streaming through her lounge windows, Marjorie looked almost stately with her halo of silvery hair and amethyst wool dress. The fire was on and colourful bunches of flowers from a variety of friends welcomed her home. Her cheeks were tinged with pink and her eyes were brighter than they had been.

'I may not have a lot of energy,' she said, ' but I'm back. Just give me a little time and I shall send this one packing!' she nodded to Iris who smiled back regardless. 'She's fussing terribly.'

'No I'm not, Mum. I'm just getting my own back. I'll just get you some tea.'

'I'm glad you came round dear,' she said patting my hand. 'I've so much to thank you for. They tell me you came regularly to hospital - I'm just sorry I don't remember all your visits.' We laughed together. 'But I do remember you bringing such a restfulness with you. I needed that. Thank you.'

'You don't need to thank me. Just keep getting better.' She said nothing, but laid her hand again on mine.

Iris nudged the door open. 'Afternoon tea is served!' she announced.

CHAPTER 16

It was a richly colourful October. For weeks the weather had been warm and dry and now as it turned colder, the changing leaves cascaded in pale gold, russet and burnt umber with the occasional slash of crimson. Iris had returned at last to Manchester, and Marjorie was on the mend.

'It's working,' I said to Sybil one night. 'I can hardly believe it.'

'The healing, you mean,' she breathed softly on the scented candle I had lit. The flame flickered. 'Why shouldn't it?'

'Well, it's hard to believe that just because you think something, it happens.'

'Does anything ever happen before it's thought about?' The candlelight illuminated her face from below and the wavering flame made her look out of the ordinary.

'Yes. It rains. Trains don't come on time. Weeds grow. I don't think about those things. They just happen. Even if I did think about them, it wouldn't change anything. That's why I'm surprised this healing seems to work.'

'Oh, it only seems to work now, does it?' She moved away from the flame and became ordinary again. 'What happened to make the change?'

'I talked to you about it,' I said without thinking.

'Precisely. You thought negatively about it and your thought had an effect. You think negatively and its power diminishes. Think positively and it grows. You've just demonstrated it for yourself.'

'But...'

'No buts,' she paced back and forth in front of me. This was going to be a lecture. 'Every plan you've ever had, every daydream, every wishful thought, every aspiration. Where do they start? Here,' she said tapping her temple with her long index finger. 'Here in your mind. First you think it. Then you clothe it in images, words and feelings until it's real here,' again she tapped her temple. 'Then you begin the activity. You ask a question, tell a friend, read a book or go to the bank. You start the ball rolling. Everything you do starts here,' she said emphatically.

'I don't question that,' I said, feeling myself gear up for a debate. 'The starting point's not the problem. It's what happens after the starting point that concerns me.' Now I wouldn't let her get a word in edgeways. 'Most of my plans, dreams, wishes and aspirations don't ever get beyond here.' I mimicked her tapping. 'They evaporate into thin air. They don't have any effect on the outside world at all. They just disappear.'

'Does your healing feel like a daydream?' Sybil retaliated, stopped me in my tracks.

'No.'

'It feels different,' she declared. 'How does it feel different?' Now she was on the attack.

I was about to say I didn't know, but it came out as 'I ... it's more focused, more directed. It's like I'm sending myself to her. Sending the light that is me ... to her.'

'I thought you said it wasn't like daydreaming. Now you're saying you're a light. Where did that notion come from?' She was still challenging and I realised quite pointedly how important it was that she didn't laugh at me. I felt very vulnerable, as if I were on the verge of sharing a secret with someone I wasn't sure I could trust. I slowed down. 'It's not a notion,' I said carefully. 'It's my experience. I know it's true because I've felt it. Lived it.'

'Invested in it.' She completed my declaration. 'You've invested your trust in that experience, haven't you? So that now when you think about healing you don't just think. You exert your will, you direct and you give. You give part of yourself. You give your power. that's why you feel vulnerable talking about it,' she added as an afterthought.

'Then you believe me?' I was relieved.

'Of course I do. Why else would I be here? It's you that's short on belief, not me.' She started to pace again, but more slowly this time. 'First you are moved to heal. You think about healing, you become healing and you give of your healing being.' She looked almost sadly at me. 'That's not daydreaming,' she said.

I breathed in deeply, relieved at her confidence in me, and became aware of the cedary scent of the candle. 'How do I reach her?' I asked.

'Like this - ' Sybil wafted her hand towards the candle. 'Think of yourself as the candle,' she said. 'The wax part is your physical body which is moulded and changed by the passage of time. The flame is the real you, your soul if you like. But look at the halo around that flame. Look at the luminosity. That's the real you radiating out. And no matter how small or feeble the flame, its radiations of light reach to the furthest corners of the room. The physical you can be stuck in its candleholder in one place, but the radiations can reach out far and wide.'

'Mm,' I pondered this for a moment.

'But think what would happen if the room suddenly ran out of oxygen,' she continued.

'The flame would go out.'

'Right. No flame. No radiation. But in terms of this room, there's an ever-flowing supply of oxygen. It keeps the flame alive and lets the light shine out.' She stood by the window for a moment, silhouetted by the moon in a clear, frosty sky. 'Its the same in spiritual matters. The universe isn't empty. It's full of energy that pulses away. You can call it prana if you like, or chi, ether or even God if that pleases you. But it's there, all round about you, feeding the flame of your soul and carrying your light upon its waves. Stray thoughts are transmitted but don't get very far - they lack your driving force behind them. But when the force of your soul drives them, they sail easily to their destination. Where they are received and accepted.' She caught my look. 'Sometimes consciously, sometimes unconsciously, but received all the same.'

I was about to ask how that helped a person to heal when she continued. 'You feared I would laugh at your light, didn't you? You were anxious that you might be foolish.' I looked down with a fleeting smile. 'And that inhibited your ability to act, to work, to use that hoped for healing.'

'Yes,' I agreed.

'And then you received my thought (through the normal channels of speech),' she added with a little laugh, 'and my approval, my agreement, my thought, changed your ability to act, to work, to use that healing.'

'Yes, I felt free to use it with confidence.' I could smile more openly now.

'That's how healing works,' she said, parting her hands as if to reveal a secret in the air between them, 'It frees the recipient to act more confidently, to allow their very life force to come into play more strongly to make the blighted part whole once again.'

Tears of pleasure sprung to my eyes.

'I must stop doing this!' I snuffled, reaching out for some paper tissues. 'You'd think I was miserable or something.'

She placed her hand on my head, almost in benediction. 'Go placidly ...' she said, and was gone.

It was the perfect night. Cold and crisp, the sky was clear as a bell. Two huge pans of home made soup were steaming away in the kitchen and wine and nibbles were at the ready. Tom, in charge of the bonfire was happy as you like shouting orders to his lieutenants about sand boxes, long matches and safe distances. Iris, Peter and the kids were up for the weekend and were already mucking in. Marjorie was coming along a bit later. A clutter of friends had arrived, wrapped up to the nines and bearing gifts of rockets, catherine wheels and sundry other explosives. Mhairi was already ladling out the soup.

It was Guy Fawkes' Night and, as Chief Dog, Balthazar had taken up residence in the shower cabinet as being the most firework free zone in the house. Caspar was wondering whether to join him when the doorbell rang once again.

'I brought you my special treacle toffee!' It was Marjorie looking for all the world like a cheery gnome, wrapped up as she was in layers of jackets and long woolly scarves. On the top of her head was a green skiing hat from some historic visit to Switzerland, and emerging from her heavy boots was an amazing pair of bright red leggings.

'Toffee!' she said again, pushing a tray of it under my nose. I accepted it gladly.

'Come in! Come in! I see you've come prepared.' I laughed and gave her a hug. She looked so well.

We chatted, laughed, sipped and sparkled our way through an hour's worth of amazing fireworks and then went inside for some serious eating. Balti and Caspar emerged from self-imposed exile and made short work of some lingering sausage rolls.

It was an undemanding, happy evening, and as our neighbours meandered their way home before midnight, I felt a glow of satisfaction that Marjorie had lasted the pace and outstayed almost everyone else.

'Come on Mum, you're holding everyone up,' Iris called, holding the front door open for her.

'It's all right. I'm not taking up residence,' she said as she reached for the pile that was her jackets and scarves. 'Thanks for a lovely evening. It was great fun. But now it's home for the gnome,' she said giving me a peck on both cheeks. 'I'll get the tray back tomorrow.'

'You mean you're going to leave me to scrape all that sticky goo off it?' Tom teased.

'But of course!' she shouted over her shoulder as she left amid the flurry of her family.

'I enjoyed that,' said Tom later as he turned out the light. 'It was like being a kid again. We must do it again next year.' I think I was already asleep.

The phone rang, dragging me from a deep sleep. I was up before I was awake and sleepwalked towards the receiver.
'It's Iris. Mum's going back into hospital.' An electric shock flashed me awake.
'What's happened?'
'We've called the ambulance. It should arrive any minute. We think she's taken a kind of stroke. I ...' her voice crackled into tears.
'I'll be right over,' I said. 'Just hang on.'
The children were sitting unnaturally quiet in the living room, watching their father's face tense with waiting. 'Go on up,' he said. 'She's with Marjorie in the front bedroom.'
The old lady in the bed was curled up on one side, her eyes closed and her mouth slightly open. She was breathing, but very shallowly. All the vibrancy and colour of yesterday was gone. Iris sat on the bed, stroking her forehead and murmuring quietly to her. I pulled up a chair.
'What happened?'
'I don't really know,' Iris continued stroking her mother's face. 'Earlier this morning I heard her moan and came through to see if she was all right. She just looked like this and moaned again. I couldn't get through to her, so I phoned Dr Fadden and as soon as he arrived he called for the ambulance.' Her eyes looked up into mine. 'She was so happy last night, so full of herself ....' I put an arm round her.
We heard the front door open and Peter talking to the ambulance men. With quick professionalism they had Marjorie wrapped up and transported downstairs. We followed on, bewildered. Iris turned back to me and Peter.
'On you go in the ambulance, love. I'll stay with the kids.'
'I'll pack a few things,' I said. 'I know where they are. I'll follow on in the car and stay with you if you like.'
'Here, take a jacket with you.' Peter handed it to her.
'Here's some sweets, you might need them.' Young Elsa hugged her Mum and pressed some fruit gums into her hand. Ricky gave her another hug and we watched the paramedic close the heavy door behind her. Back in the hall, the house seemed empty. I packed a case for Marjorie once again and left Peter with Elsa and Ricky. Tom came round with some soup for lunch, and I took my leave.

In a waiting area, Iris told me how she had sat with her mum in one of the individual rooms. Marjorie's hand seemed clamped to hers and she wouldn't let go.

57

'They had to examine her,' she said. 'I had to leave. I had to prise her fingers from me.'
'You'll be able to go back soon. Don't worry,' I said. 'She'll be OK. Don't worry.'
We sat together. Worrying.

The next three days seemed out of time. Some tests were done. Fragments of reports were made by kindly nurses, doctors, specialists. We took turns to sit for quiet hours, wiping her face, smoothing a pillow, holding her hand. Always looking for a sign of returning consciousness. Always looking.
Sometimes I talked softly to her, mulling over old memories, telling her what a good friend she was, surmising what kind of lives Elsa and Ricky might have as their talents blossomed. There was no reply, but I felt she was listening and, well, I needed that.
On the second morning, Iris came in in the middle of one of my monologues. She looked taken aback. 'Do you think she can hear you?' she asked. 'I hope so,' I said. 'If she can, she needs company. It must be lonely in there when you can't speak and see.' Iris was hesitant. 'Try it and see for yourself,' I said. 'Tell her all you've ever wanted to tell her. I'll leave you for a while.'
When Peter arrived, we went in together.
'She squeezed my hand,' said Iris tearfully. 'It wasn't strong, but I'm sure she did. I'm sure she can hear us.' So we chatted on, and waited and watched.
About eight o'clock that evening, I sat in to give the other two a break. I was half-heartedly reading a magazine when I sense her breathing was changing. As I looked up, Iris and Peter came back. I nodded for them to watch Marjorie carefully. Iris leaned over and spoke close to her face. 'Mum. Mum, can you hear me?' For a special moment, she opened her eyes wide. 'Mum?' She was looking through Iris, beyond her. Her face lit up in disbelief and sheer pleasure. 'Sam! Sam - I don't believe it! Oh, you've come.' And with a sigh, she sank back on the pillows.
'Quick, get the nurse!' Peter shouted.
I ran into the corridor and reached out to a passing nurse. 'Please, come quickly!'
At the bedside she checked for a pulse, listened for a heartbeat. Everything was preternaturally still. 'Mrs Fellows, I'm sorry. Your Mum has passed away.'

CHAPTER 18

The bleak November chill was appropriate for the funeral. At the funeral parlour, all Marjorie's many friends turned out to say their last farewell. The Rev. Walters had known her quite well, and was able to personalise an otherwise impersonal ceremony. Everyone was touched by the intimate little tokens her grandchildren placed on her coffin - flowers with little hand-written notes.

The journey to the Crematorium was followed by more formalities and hymn singing. After that was the buffet in a local hotel. Peter had got it all organised, and we moved from one stage to another like clockwork dolls. The absence of Marjorie's fun and informality made it all the more poignant. Iris was coping well by being somehow a million miles away from it all.

It wasn't until a few days later when I was helping her to clear the house that I felt I was truly in contact with her again. We'd been piling clothes into black plastic bags to take to the Salvation Army when I declared a tea break. I went off to put the kettle on, and Iris followed me with a pile of family photo albums.

'I haven't looked at these for years,' she said. 'It's like going back in time as I flick over the pages. Look at this one,' she said. 'Don't they look young and full of hope?' It was a picture of her Mum and Dad - a forties wedding picture in black and white. Sam was in his early twenties and just out of the army. He still had that military stance in the photo, standing proud in his double-breasted suit with shoes absolutely gleaming. Marjorie looked petite and very pretty. Her pale wedding suit was just to below the knee, the jacket shoulder-padded and skimming her neat hips. She wore a corsage of what looked like orchids and a hat which defied description.

'Just look at that hat!' Iris said. 'We often used to tease her about that. There were fashion victims even then.' We laughed as she continued to turn over the pages - holiday snaps, dances, an operatic society do, babies, family snaps, more holidays. A lifetime unfurled.

'Your Dad's name was Sam, wasn't it?' I was checking up.

'Yes,' said Iris, 'yes it was.'

'Marjorie mentioned him often, but she always called him Dad,' I said. 'I just wasn't sure.'

'Yes, I'm afraid I was their main aim in life. They so much wanted a family and when my elder brother died of appendicitis, they'd to wait years for me to come along. There must have been twelve years between us. They were just family people .... and so proud when we had our two.' She gazed into the silence, remembering. 'Do you think she saw him?' Now her gaze was on me.

'In the hospital, you mean?' She nodded. 'I hardly dare say. But it looked like it, didn't it?'

'Yes. She came so alive again, just for that minute. I'd like to think she did. Oh, I'm getting weepy again,' she said and gulped. 'Do you think people might live on, you know, after they've died? Do you think it's possible? She seemed so convinced, so certain.'

'Iris, you're asking such impossible questions. I've nothing to answer you with. If there's any love in the world, any God, then surely we wouldn't just disappear like this year's leaves. I'd love to think souls lived on in some alternative universe and that we could catch up with them eventually. I'd love to think that. That no one was really lost to us. But, ...' she stopped me. 'Do you know what keeps me going just now? The idea that he came for her. You know. The idea that he was only a little further along the road, and now that he knows the way, he came back so that they could start out again together. Just like they were in that old photo. That's what's keeping me going. Is that stupid?'

'No.' What else could I say?

'It's what I tell Ricky and Elsa. I tell them gran's got a new life with papa now and that they're happy together, because they missed each other so much.'

'I know. There's no harm in that Iris. No harm and a lot of love.'

'But there's something else. You know how Elsa's only six?'

'Yes.'

'Well she was giggling away to herself in her bedroom the other morning and I asked her what she was laughing at. She said she was laughing at papa because he was doing that funny thing with his arm again. I asked her what she meant because she was only a baby when he died. She tried to show me but said she couldn't do it - his arm went further back than hers.' She stopped for a moment, waiting for my reaction. 'You see, he was double jointed and he used to make me laugh as a child by monkeying about like that.'

'So you think ...' she interrupted me.

'So I asked Elsa if he'd said anything. And she said yes, "Tell Mummy it's OK. I've got Marjie." But to tell you the truth, she was more impressed with the arm trick!' She pushed the photos away. 'So that's what's keeping me going. Come on. Let's finish those black bags.'

'Tell me about life after death,' I said to Tom over our evening meal.

'It's what happens after a day's work's done,' he retaliated.

'No, seriously, what do you think?'

'Is this about Marjorie?'

60

'Well, yes partly,' and I told him Iris' story.

'She might be right, I suppose. I hope she is, but I've no way of knowing. What does Sybil say?'

I felt he was poking at me. I was never quite sure whether he took Sybil seriously or not. But he was prepared to put up with her (or prepared to put up with me talking about her) and I respected him for that. I felt a bit irked as well. Not with Tom, but perhaps with me. Throughout the trauma of the previous couple of weeks I'd felt angry, betrayed, let down, over-dependent, doubt-ridden - you name it! And I hadn't meditated at all. I'd run away from it. I was so disappointed. Disappointed that the healing didn't work. That I couldn't magic problems away.

Now, like a child caught playing truant, I was reluctant to return to face the music.

CHAPTER 19

'There's no such thing as magic.' Duster in hand, I half heartedly ran it round Magnus's picture. Opus the cat rubbed itself against his shins and purred, 'I've been trying to tell him that for years, but all he says is I'm a materialist and wouldn't understand.' His tail twirled in pleasure. 'That's a strange description for an animal with nine lives.'

'Maybe it makes you nine times more materialistic.'

'I never thought of it like that,' said Opus, smoothing his whiskers out against his master's leg.

'That's because you never think,' said the voice above him. 'How am I supposed to concentrate with all this chat going on?'

'Don't ask me... I never think!' returned the cat, weaving his way between Magnus' sandalled feet. 'Ask her.' His hazel eyes peered at me defiantly. 'Well?'

'What are you concentrating on anyway?' I asked.

'First you interrupt me and then you expect an explanation from me. This is ridiculous!' He stuffed his baton in one pocket and the bewildered frog in the other. His long arms hung down, ending strangely in clenched fists, and he continued to glare at me under an angry frown.

'Magic is ridiculous! You're wasting your time.' I was truculent.

His eyes narrowed for a moment, as if a wisp of smoke had irritated them. Still he looked at me. He sat down deliberately in a controlled sort of way and hardly noticed as Opus used him as a short cut, running diagonally across his lap, up onto his shoulder and from there to the back of the chair. 'I see you better now,' he said, sitting wide-legged and leaning towards me. He smelt vaguely of sandalwood. He clasped his long twiglike fingers and looking beyond them at my still-to-be-vacuumed carpet said, 'You're sick.'

'Sick and tired, perhaps, but not deluded!' I snapped at his insult. It had no effect on him.

'Good,' he said, 'that's a first. You see, you're improving already.'

'You're nothing but make-believe!'

'No. That's not so good,' he countered. 'Let's go back to the previous response.'

'Can you see what was good about your previous response?'

Opus butted in. 'I can't, because I don't think.' He began to scrop the back of the chair with his claws. I flicked at him with my duster. Magnus sneezed and his eyes watered. Opus strolled along the chair back, wound his tail round the tip of the magician's celestial hat and purred in a most satisfactory manner. 'He's allergic to dust, don't you know.' He blinked once and settle down again. Magnus meanwhile was playing the trumpet voluntary into an antique handkerchief produced from his pocket.

'Sorry,' I said.

Nose blowing and eye mopping finished, he gulped at the air and started again. Patiently. 'Communication depends on one statement being listened to and then responded to directly. When you speak along your own line without responding to mine, you use words to destroy, not create, the link of life. That's what communication is, you know.' He looked without peering now. 'It's a life flow when it works. And life is creative.'

'And creativity is magic,' added Opus.

'I though you didn't believe in magic?'

'Oh, I wouldn't trust a thing I say, if I were you.' He curled himself up precariously on the top of the chair back, and turned his grey head sideways so that one eye seemed directly over the other.

'So when I said you were sick,' continued Magnus, 'I wasn't insulting you, I was coming to a conclusion based on your reaction to my words. You didn't respond to them. Instead you barged on with your own line. When you respond, that's creative and healthy. When you ignore, you destroy and that's sick.' Now it was my turn to peer at him. 'You think life hasn't listened to you, don't you?' I said nothing. 'So now you're intent on not listening back. You're aggressive and challenging. And in my book, that's a dis-ease.'

'And in mine, that's a figure of fun,' said Opus with only his lower eye open.

'So perhaps you'd like to start our conversation again,' Magnus encouraged.

'I can't remember how we started.'

'I asked how I was expected to concentrate with all this chat going on.'

'OK,' I said, stringing along, 'then I'll say I'm sorry for interrupting you. I didn't think talking to your cat would cause you to be distracted.'

'Then I'll go on staring at you because I've forgotten where I'd got to.'

'And I'll politely enquire whether you were concentrating on some magic.'

'And because you're polite, I'll answer you. Yes.'

'Could you spare the time to tell me about what you do. You see, I don't think I believe in magic although I once wanted to.'

'Good,' said Magnus. 'Now you are listening before you respond. I can feel that. And that makes me want to respond in a creative way too. That's much better. In fact, you're quite likeable now.'

'Just quite likeable?'

'And you're listening carefully. Well done.' He sat back and rubbed his knees approvingly with his boney hands.

'But you haven't answered my request,' I said, 'to...'

63

'And you're intent on keeping the life flowing. My, what a rapid improvement!' His feet danced in his sandals.

'Magnus! Now you're doing what I was doing.'

'And you can feel the frustration that first made me angry, can't you?' he beamed, settling down again. 'Listening to life and responding to what you hear. That's magic. Speaking to life and listening to its response. That's magic. You only learned half the lesson, so you lost the magic,' he said with a sigh.

'What do you mean?'

Opus rotated his head to normal once again. 'What he means is you learned to watch life, but then you started barking orders at it without asking whether it wanted to be barked at. Nothing,' he lifted his grey body into an arch and bottle-brushed his tail,' ever wants to be barked at. Believe me.'

'I just wanted the healing to work. That's not barking orders.'

'It might be when it goes against nature,' Magnus said softly. He thought for a moment and then pulled out a little round seed from his pocket. It was a sweet pea. He rolled it around in the hollow of his lean palm. 'Look,' he said. 'That's whole isn't it? And perfect.'

'Yes, in its own way.'

'But if it stayed that way forever - round and brown - would that be perfection?'

'I don't know what you're getting at. What are you leading up to?' He rolled it round his palm once more, and when it came to rest, the brown covering had split. I could see the white underneath and the beginnings of a root.

'Where would be the life in it if it never changed?' he asked. 'Its perfection lies in its unfoldment. Look.' Now the root was a fine feathery network and the seed had sprouted a pale green shoot. 'Healing works with nature, not against it. When the time for change and growth comes, work with it - not against it. Don't hold it back, move forward with it. Look!' he laughed. His left hand clasped over the right and then unclasped. The roots grew between his fingers and the shoot became darker green leaves.

I gasped (in a restrained sort of way of course) 'How do you...'

'Don't bark, harmonise,' said Opus as he strolled in front of Magnus' hands, 'Meeeowww...'

'Until the end is achieved,' said Magnus with a flourish, presenting me with a fully formed sweet pea, pale pink edged with white. 'Beautiful,' he said more to himself than me. 'Work with nature, not against it...'

I raised the flower to my nostrils to drink in its perfume. I was in for a surprise. 'Oh,' I said, 'it smells strangely of sandalwood.'

'What did you expect?' said Opus following his master back into the picture, 'Magic?'

I thought I'd put the sweet pea in some fibre in a pot on the kitchen windowsill. It was the wrong time of year for it to flourish, but I wanted to watch it to see what happened next. 'Look what I've got, Caspar,' I said, proud of my trophy. I laid it down beside me while I filled a little pot on the back door step.

'What are you potting up, love?' Tom was standing in the doorway.

'It's a curious thing,' I said, turning round to show him. Caspar nuzzled in to me and sniffed at the pot. 'Look, it's a ...' The plant was gone.

Tom laughed. 'I think maybe Caspar was the last to appreciate it,' he said. 'Have you seen those spark plugs I bought the other day?'

'They're in the blue dish on the windowsill,' I answered absently.

Just a couple of weeks after New Year, I tumbled into the kitchen with bags full of bits and pieces. There was no blue dish.

'What's happened to the little dish?' I asked Tom as I heaved the bags on to the kitchen table.

'What dish?' he replied, engrossed in his newspaper.

'The little ceramic one on the windowsill.'

'Oh, the cat knocked it over. I swept it up and put the remains in the bucket.'

'What cat? We don't have a cat.'

'The smoky one from next door. It paid us a visit this morning.'

'I didn't know next door had a cat,' I interrupted.

'Well, you know now,' he smiled back. 'The dogs spotted it, so it made a pretty hasty exit, and took the dish with it, so to speak. I junked the remains. In the bin.'

'Oh,' I started to put the shopping away. 'So it lives in Marjorie's old house?'

'Yes, with Kenneth and Isobel, your new neighbours. I had a chat to them for the first time this morning. They're settling in fine. No kids, just the cat.' He returned smugly to his newspaper. 'We've been invited over tomorrow night for a drink,' he added just when I thought the news bulletin was over. 'I said we'd go over about eight. OK?'

'It's too soon,' I thought to myself. It seemed no time at all since I had been clearing the house with Iris. The place had sold almost as soon as it had been put on the market and suddenly there were new people in Marjorie's house. It didn't seem right somehow. Yet I knew I was being foolish. What was the point in it standing empty? Why shouldn't the new couple want to move in and start their New Year there? Things moved on and I should too. I was annoyed with myself.

An array of huge, exotic plants filled the bay window. We had settled into a capacious deep blue settee with bright turquoise and cream cushions. The new carpet was wheat coloured - very plain - and an Aztec rug in the same blue, turquoise and cream with touches of terracotta was spread in front of the fireplace. Isobel was pouring drinks.

'Of course, we've everything still to do,' she said over her shoulder,' but we were dying to get in for the New Year. It's such a welcoming house.' You could see her pleasure in her new home. She snuggled into the armchair by the fire.

'I see you've got the coal fire going again,' said Tom. 'It makes such a difference, doesn't it?'

'I'm in charge of that,' Ken chipped in. 'I haven't had a fire like this since I was a kid. It's great. We'd a bit of bother getting rid of the old gas fire, but it was definitely worth it.' He picked a log out of a wicker basket near the hearth and placed it carefully on the fire where the flames would lick round it. Their cat lay on the arm of the chair opposite Isobel's. It was smoky grey with a white mask and three white paws. Not like Opus at all, I thought. It purred as Ken sat down to stroke it.

Conversation flowed easily. He was in social work and she was a physiotherapist. They were in their early thirties and full of enthusiasm for their new home. We had a guided tour. I saw pale cedar furniture where there had been dark mahogany. Unexpected curtains clashed with familiar carpets; CD racks sprouted from corners; plants in ethnic pots were everywhere.

A computer dominated the spare room where posters quarrelled with Marjorie's floral wallpaper. 'This'll be Ken's office once it's been gutted,' said Isobel with a flourish. I reminded myself she wasn't being heartless at all. The eau de nil bathroom was already vivid mediterranean blue. And plans - what plans they had! Their energy was infectious and we enjoyed our evening.

My old friend was fading from the house. There were flickers of her here and there, but they would soon be gone. I tried to think of Magnus and his lesson of change, willing myself to let go gently and move into the future that was so enticing for my new neighbours. For the first time in my life, I doubted whether it could be like that for me too.

As the New Year matured, I was more aware than usual of nostalgia and looking back. I indulged in seeing the good things in the past, and wondering (if I was honest) a little bleakly about the future.

'A mid-life crisis isn't compulsory you know.' It was the day before Burns' Night and Sybil had caught me munching peanuts. The tv was off and Tom, who had been reading an exotic, tv chef cookery book, had fallen asleep under the strain of it all.

The 'mid-life' bit rankled a little. 'It's hardly a crisis,' I snapped peevishly.

'What you mean is it's hardly mid-life.' She sat down on the footstool in front of the fire, careful to avoid Balthazar's paws twitching in a dream. 'But you don't really expect me to believe that, do you? How long do you expect to last? Seventy, eighty, ninety years?'

'Sybil, I...'

'Then you're certainly half way, maybe more.' I felt got at.

'Why the full frontal attack?' I said. I finished my peanuts and waited for her to continue.

'You need told. Instead of footering around and avoiding the issue, you need to face the facts. Then perhaps we can get on.' She sounded like my mother waiting for me to get ready for school.

'You're not a child any more,' she said perceptively.

'OK, OK. Nor a teenager, nor a first time house buyer, not upwardly mobile, famous or notorious.... So what? What do you want me to be?' She looked at me in a way that told me she wasn't going to answer. 'It's too late to be the Mother Earth figure or even the Matriarch. So what's it to be, Crone Wisdom or Bag Lady?' I felt exasperated by her. She'd 'set me off' and I'd obliged - like a rocket.

'What are you so upset about?' she said, softly stroking Balti's dreaming head. Emotion was creeping into the back of my throat.

'Oh, I don't know,' I lied. 'You spend so much of your life striving to get somewhere, to do your best. Just to build a life and achieve something. And it all just goes so quickly, doesn't it?' In spite of myself my eyes were filling up with tears. 'In a month Marjorie's belongings were packed up and re-distributed. In another her home was sold and possessed. In a third she will be gone without trace. Her efforts, her hopes and dreams - all gone in a season.' I stopped, realising how morbid this sounded, then went on regardless. 'We're all the same, aren't we? It's just, well, such a disappointment.'

'Now I understand,' said Sybil wisely. 'Marjorie was her house, her furniture, her possessions. You're bound to be upset.' She could be so patronising.

'No, of course that's not the case. Her things just - I don't know - reflected the person she was. And the reflection is all we've got left.'

'Ah, so it's the reflection you're grieving over.'

'No it's not!' I felt myself provoked again. 'You know and I know I'm grieving over the loss of a friend. I'm sad because I know I'll lose more friends and one day I'll die too. That's what I'm grieving over. And I'm grieving over the loss of reflections - remains - things - because when they're there I can feel something of my friend lingers, and when they're gone, I know nothing does. Does that satisfy you, or are you going to tell me what I really mean again?' Before she could reply, I grabbed the remote control and pointed it at the tv. I shot it into action. Tom jerked awake as the music boomed out.

'The News,' I said. 'It's time for the News. I'll just make us some supper,' and escaped from further questioning.

CHAPTER 21

It was February. The road sparkled with frost and every spike of grass was individually carved out of crystal. The dogs moved quickly in the cold air, their warm breath drifting in silky clouds in the bright sunlight. I crunched my way over the field, aiming for the stile at the far side. The landscape and the cloudless sky seemed to be wiped clean. It was a good day and I was wrapped up warmly against the cold.

I remembered many a walk like this, across the fields and up Major's Hill. When I was still at school, Dad and I used to take our black Labrador Joel and watch him chase rabbits into the woodland at the foot of the hill. He never caught one, but he always thought he would.

'It's the chase that matters,' Dad would say. 'He wouldn't know what to do with a rabbit if he caught one.' Today my two dogs chased each other, rough-and-tumbling their way over frosty hummocks, oblivious to anything but the fun they were having. 'Dogs are hedonists,' I remember Dad saying. 'Pure pleasure-seekers, and none the worse for that. Look at the pleasure they give us,' and we'd watch Joel stop bemused and gaze at the space where a rabbit had been, then gallop off regardless to follow a new scent. 'Carefree. Focused on the now. Just like a golfer!' and he would laugh, making fun of his consuming passion.

Caspar jumped the fence. Balthazar needed some encouragement to get through. Then I clambered over the stile, carefully avoiding the barbed wire that wasn't supposed to be there. For a moment, I leant on the post and looked back over the field we'd walked through. There was a river at the foot of the field, and in the summer, standing in the shade of the trees by the stile, we used to stand still and watch for dragon flies.

'Just gaze over the field,' Dad would say. 'Don't look for anything in particular. Just gaze.' As a serious little girl, I would do just that. 'And when you see a disturbance, follow it!' he'd say. 'It'll be a dragon fly!' He was right.

'Just gaze,' said his voice. 'And when you see a disturbance, it'll be me.' I caught a flash of his face in the clear winter sunlight. Smiling. Just like he did when I saw a dragonfly. How could it be? I felt my heart thump in my chest. How could it be?

Something rustled behind me. Caspar dropped a stick at my feet and was waiting expectantly.

It couldn't be. I picked up the stick and threw it back towards the field. Back to the glimpse of a memory.

Now both dogs raced to retrieve the stick, skidding round to pick it up at speed. Caspar got there first. Balti kept on running as if getting the stick had

68

been the last thing on his mind. 'Come on boy!' I shouted. 'It's the chase that counts!' as Caspar returned, munching his way through his trophy. This time Balti needed no extra encouragement to get back through the fence.

As you make your way up the hill, following the path worn by dog walkers like me, you can linger amid clumps of trees or sit out in the open on odd boulders warn smooth by visitors taking in the view of the distant town. It is an accommodating place, its slopes easy on the legs and its views easy on the eyes. I decided to walk right to the top.

So through the trees and round boulders we went, the dogs weaving their way in front of me, sometimes following a notion of their own, but always returning. Near the top I realised I hadn't seen Balti for a while. I called him. No response. I called again. This time I heard a reply, but not what I was expecting.

'Balti it is you! Balti! Balti! Come and see what we've got. Come on boy.' Reaching the top, I could see the path on the other side. Iris was shouting, while Elsa and Ricky were in front of her chasing a young Old English Sheepdog. Typically, Balti waited for it to come to him.

'Iris, is this yours?' I said, laughing at the sight of this family in chaos. 'Where's Pete?'

'Yes,' she said, puffing a little on her way up. 'It's a rescue dog - too boisterous for its original family, they told us. We're trying to wear him out.'

'Is that me or the dog you're talking about?' Pete came into view holding an empty dog collar and a new lead.

'You're worn out already,' said Elsa, 'so it must be Rumble Mum's talking about.'

'Rumble?' I said.

'Don't ask!' said Iris.

'It's a great name!' shouted Ricky with his fists full of Rumble's long white coat. He'd captured his pet and was delighted with himself.

'Pete had a few days to take, so we thought we'd come up and get some real fresh air. We've had some good times up here,' she said looking around. 'And I want them to keep in touch with their roots.'

'Yes,' I said, 'there's a few friendly ghosts round here. Why don't you all come back and have a meal with us?' Rumble refused to be collared for long and charged back down the hill after Caspar and Balti. Ricky elected to be leader of this gang and Elsa decided against being cool, and joined the mob.

'I think the dog was a good idea,' I said as we made our way back down along the path towards the field.

'So do I, ' said Iris, 'if you're not too much into designer homes!' We chatted our way back down the hill, over the field and into my car. It was a bit of a squash, but I agreed to take Pete back to his so we could all go home together.

Elsa, Ricky and Rumble decanted back into Pete's car, and I led the way back home.

'I've got a challenge for you,' said Iris once we were alone.

'Oh? What's that?' I asked.

'Come down for a weekend in March. Tom and Pete can go fishing and you and I can go on a Psychic Development weekend.'

'You're joking!' I said, most ungraciously when I think about it. 'About the Psychic bit, I mean.'

'No I'm not. I read about it in last week's local paper. I really fancy it, and you're the ideal person to come with me. I realised it as soon as I saw Balti today.'

I pulled into the drive, with Pete close behind. The conversation was overcome by barking dogs and excited children. We tumbled into our hallway amidst shouts of, 'Where's the chef?' and 'Watch the dogs!'

Monopoly was well underway when Iris and I escaped into the kitchen to get some peace and quiet.

'So what is this psychic thing then?' I asked, piling plates up and sorting out the cutlery.

'Oh, you'll love it.' Iris was absolutely certain. 'It's a two day seminar in a local hotel and its run by a clairvoyant consultant. She's supposed to be quite good.'

'Clairvoyant. Isn't that like fortune telling?' I started on the dishes - that didn't sound like something I'd love.

'No. She's a sensitive. You know, a medium. I've seen her working once before. She's really interesting.' Iris wasn't giving up.

'I know you hope Marjorie's still somewhere about...' I paused. 'Did you get a message from this medium then?'

'No, but she did give some messages to other people in the audience. It's not as crazy as you think.' She stopped drying and looked at me. 'You will come, won't you? I don't want to go on my own.'

'Iris, this could be a total wild goose chase ...' I wasn't keen.

'Well, hunt a wild goose or two with me!' Her tone was light but her eyes were serious.

I gave in. 'OK, if the fishermen agree to be baby-sitters. And dog sitters.'

'Of course they will!' she lightened up and went through to announce her victory.

CHAPTER 22

Decorating the back bedroom had started off as a vague notion and grown into a sort of passion all of its own. I think it was a creative alternative to spring cleaning which Tom was prepared to condone as long as he could have nothing to do with it. That suited me fine.

In the cold dank days of late February, it was a cheerful option and I even took pleasure in clearing, stripping and washing down ... doing it by the book. Glossing round the windows was mindlessly reassuring and reduced me to an acquiescent state of mind.

'I'm sorry I got angry with you,' I thought laconically to Sybil. 'You touched a raw nerve, I suppose. But maybe it's thickening over now.' No response. I took another brushful of paint and continued working away. 'This self awareness caper isn't comfortable. It lets you away with nothing. And it's hard facing things you want to avoid. I am half way through my life and I've only just got round to trying to understand it, or me - or both. Aargh!' I got paint on the window pane and reached for the cloth to wipe it away. 'But at least it lets me know I'm alive and thinking.' This time the paint flowed neatly to the join. Smart. I stopped to look at it. It was dark outside and I could see my face reflected in the glass. Above it, to the right, was another - Sybil's. 'Oh, you're there,' I said, pleasantly surprised. 'I thought I was talking to myself.'

'You never do that,' said the face in the glass, with the hint of a smile. 'So is it Crone Wisdom or Bag Lady who's alive? ... I think that's where we left off.' She was almost diplomatic.

'Neither,' I said, smoothing out my brush strokes. 'I've decided they're other people's categories - footprints I've already made in the sand. Or maybe even footprints I've still to make.'

'Oh?' said Sybil looking over my shoulder.

'But the footprints - they don't matter. Making the journey is what counts. The footprints will wear away, but the journey keeps going.'

'You've missed a bit.'

'You mean the journey - well, that's my unfolding experience, and my awareness of it. That's what keeps going.'

'I didn't mean that!' she said. 'Up an inch or so and to your right. You've missed a bit.' I brushed over it. 'That's better. You really shouldn't paint in electric light, you know. You can never see properly.'

'I thought you were my spiritual mentor,' I said, turning round. 'Why are you giving me painting lessons?'

She snorted. 'It's perfectly obvious. I'm an interfering busybody.' I laughed in agreement. 'Besides which,' she added, 'your differentiation between the physical and the spiritual is purely arbitrary. Why draw any line between them? Why make them different when they're all part of the same spectrum?'

'You're not going to tell me painting and decorating is a spiritual exercise.'

'Of course I am! Who is doing it?'

'I am.'

'You're a spiritual being, aren't you?'

'Well, yes.'

'And how are you doing it? Beautifully, thoughtfully, carelessly, angrily?'

'Happily,' I replied, 'and thoughtfully.'

'Are those purely physical attributes?'

'No. They describe my state of mind.'

'Or even your state of being,' she concluded. 'So in that sense, your work is spiritual work, whatever you are doing.' Without a pause she continued. 'So it doesn't matter what you do in life, great or small, significant or trivial, paid or unpaid, it is how you do it that matters. How you live determines what your spiritual nature will be. The physical end product is insignificant.'

'So it doesn't matter if I miss a bit or not,' I said, pointing to the paintwork.

She sighed, 'It is not the measure of you. The outer world is not concerned whether the window is painted or not. But to the inner world, whether you care enough to do the best you can - that's significant.'

I rested my brush on the edge of the paint can.

'It's the chase that matters ....' she said, mimicking. I was slightly taken aback.

'Sybil, in the field that day, were you there?'

'Where else would I be?' she answered with a question.

'Then, did...'

'You're brush is dripping paint,' she said.

'Are you always there - where I am?' She looked at me in a non-committal sort of way. Each met the other's gaze in an adolescent staring game. I took a breath, 'Sybil, are you real?'

'That depends what you mean by real,' she replied.

'No, seriously. Just give me a straight answer.'

'Yes.'

I stared at her again, wondering what I wanted to say. 'Then where are you?'

'In your consciousness. And your back bedroom, of course.'

'But you're not in the bedroom in the same sense that I am?'

'No. If someone else walked in, they'd think you were talking to yourself.'

'But I'm not talking to myself.' That was half a question, half a statement.

72

'No.' I waited for an explanation, but none came.

'You could be a sub personality of mine.'

'Or you could be a sub personality of mine, which seems more likely to me. Although I'd like to think I could be more creative than that.'

'That sounded as if it could be an insult, Sybil.'

'But you know it wasn't because you feel quite comfortable with it, don't you? More amused than offended.' She smiled. 'So tell me what I am then. I'm dying to know.' There was a pause while I thought. 'Go on,' she encouraged. 'Tell me my options!'

'Well,' I began, 'you could be a character created by me - like an author creates characters in a book.'

'OK. But why would you create a character when you weren't writing a book?'

'Perhaps because I was lonely, or bored maybe.'

'So were you lonely or bored?' she asked.

'I don't think so. Maybe you're part of my character that I've repressed for years and now you've burst back into my conscious mind after all that time tucked away.'

'So what is there about me that's the sort of thing you'd repress? Am I socially unacceptable, revolutionary, rude?'

'You are a bit blunt sometimes.'

'I am the honest open side of your character then? Have you been repressing that all these years?' I smiled ruefully.

'You could be my conscience,' I ventured.

'When was the last time I berated you about the amount you spend on clothes, not re-cycling your rubbish, getting petty at work,'

'OK, OK! Maybe you're on a work to rule! Could you be my higher self?' Sybil looked blank. 'What's that?'

'I don't really know. The finer part of me, my better side, my wiser aspect ...' My inspiration faded.

'Well, at least that's an improvement on a sub personality.' Sybil grinned. 'Any other options?'

'My guardian angel?'

'I've no wings.'

'My guide?'

'No map, no walking boots.'

'Then I've no idea! I give in.' I leant on the windowsill and watched Sybil as she took over the conversation.

'Answer me this then. Do you always know when I'll appear?'

'No, sometimes you take me by surprise.'

'Can you predict what I'm going to say next?'

73

'Only now and then.'

'Do you always understand what I say?'

'You know I don't.'

'Do you always agree with what I say?'

'Ditto!'

'Then could you accept that although I am in your consciousness, I am not your consciousness? .... not part of you? ... You look doubtful,' she added.

'I suppose what you say is just about possible, I don't know how it could work, that's all.'

'Well, maybe just before you unstick your elbow from the pool of paint it's resting in, you could just agree to think about that in the meantime,' she suggested.

I looked down. Sure enough, paint had been dripping from the brush and had formed a sticky little pool in the middle of which was my elbow. 'Oh Sybil! You might have told me!' I shrieked.

'I seem to remember saying something about paint dripping,' she said, but already I wasn't listening.

CHAPTER 23

It wasn't hard finding the hotel. It was one of a national chain and was easily accessible from the motorway. Rather unfairly, I had expected it to be something nearer a run down Victorian boarding house, but here we were, Iris and I, in the Hotel Reception, reading the Welcome Board which informed us that Psychic Development was in the Martingdale Suite.

All the way down the M6 I had kept asking myself why I was doing this, and the best excuse I could come up with was that I was keeping Iris company - for Marjorie's sake. I suspect Tom took it to be another aspect of the Mid Life Crisis, which he had tastefully abbreviated to 'milk' and to which he attributed all odd notions of mine. I was happy to play along with this, as 'milk' provided an ever-ready excuse for getting away with various brands of murder.

Anyway, despite or because of this, Iris and I found ourselves signing in and being provided with badges and programmes. Inside the conference room, coffee, mineral water and herb tea were laid out while people milled around. I became uncomfortable with my bias, realising I was expecting to see Magnus look-alikes and have-been Flower Children.

At first glance, most people looked normal and the ages ranged from twenty something to nearly seventy something. On closer inspection, quite a few wore pendants formed from crystals tied inside silver spirals. Here and there I'd spot little Red Indian pouches, or long earrings. But surprisingly enough, the New Age clutter was balanced up with clipboards and notepads. I felt reassured. I pinned on my badge, balanced my coffee on my programme and tried to look psychic.

Then I thought enigmatic might be safer.

An organiser approached us. 'Hi, I'm Jill. Glad you could come. Have you been in development long?' Jill was in her thirties and looked as if she might work in personnel. She was fair haired and breezy in jeans and a sweatshirt, and I was telling myself not be afraid of her.

'No, we're brand new to this,' said Iris, obviously not frightened at all,' so tell us what we have to do.'

'Well, over there you will see my colleague, Maggie,' she pointed to a plump woman in her fifties, dressed in layers of russet - wide trousers, over-blouse and floor-length coat. 'Once everyone's gathered together, we'll split you into beginners and advanced. We'll start in about ten minutes,' she said blithely. 'Just mingle. The bookstall's over there.'

My reassurance was short-lived. 'Are you really sure you want to do this?' I said, scuttling after Iris as she targeted the stall. 'There's still time to leave. We could still...'

'Wow! look at this,' was her reply. She handed me 'I Have Lived Before' with Egyptian hieroglyphs emblazoned on the cover, and 'Channelling for Mother Earth - an Environmentalist's guide to the Cosmos'. A shadowy female profile was set against the backdrop of a silvery moon. Ambient music mewed softly in the background and the scent of aromatic candles wafted towards me. Packs of cards promised a future, instant wisdom was packaged in little books of wise sayings. Silks, crystals, wind chimes and singing Tibetan bowls were there in profusion. Through it all, two slender girls in black tee shirts and jeans, padded softly on sandal-clad feet, offering advice and wrapping up newly bought treasures with silver-ringed fingers.

I was a wide-eyed child in a fair ground waiting for the harpies.

There was a tug at my sleeve. 'We'd better go or we'll miss the start.' Iris pulled me into line and I followed her to where the audience/students were sitting down. There must have been sixty of us altogether. Maggie and Jill, both psychic consultants, were joined on their raised platform by another two workers : John, a 'well-known clairvoyant' in a Pringle jumper and slacks, and Hillary described as 'a natural medium' who was in her sixties and traditionally dressed in co-ordinates.

An 'ice-breaking' exercise had the effect of separating me from Iris and depositing me in 'Group One' which was for absolute beginners. Despite my best efforts I was herded into a side room with my group, and reassured that we'd all meet up before lunch. Hillary was in charge. She told us we were going to do ribbons. 'These are ribbons,' she said, lifting a strip of heavy card to which were attached maybe forty strips of brightly coloured satin ribbon of every shade and hue. She shook out their folds. Each piece was about two feet long.

'Now just watch,' she said. I waited, anticipating a conjuring trick. Instead, she approached a tired-looking man in his fifties and asked him to pick three ribbons - any three that appealed to him. He picked egg-yolk yellow, dark green and a chestnutty brown.

'Now then dear,' she began, 'let's look at the yellow. It's a bright, rich colour, indicating a lively mind and a thoughtful nature, but to me, it's out of place. You thought you had established your position in life, didn't you, but recently you've been plucked right out of that stable situation and you feel extremely vulnerable.'

'That's right,' he said,

'I know it is,' she agreed. 'In fact, you have worried that you will not be able to cope. That in fact, you might not even survive. But you will you know. You faced a similar situation oh, maybe twenty years ago, and it turned out for the best didn't it?'

He looked surprised and then said yes.

'In fact you made a good living out of that enforced change, didn't you?' He smiled, but she didn't look up from the ribbons this time. 'Well, this green tells me not only are you at the top of the tree in your working life, you are held in great respect by your colleagues. It's a very dignified colour,' she said to herself, stroking the ribbon, 'and it is not about to fade. Indeed neither your reputation nor your bank balance is under any threat, believe me.' She peered at him now. 'You are about to make a contact (within the next four days I should say) and as a result of that, you will begin a new business venture which will create subsidiaries world wide. You know what I'm talking about, don't you?' This time, the man nodded slowly, saying nothing. 'Then go ahead with your plan, but don't let Robert have anything to do with it. Is that clear?'

The man coughed. 'I can't believe that!' he said.

'What can't you believe, dear?' Hillary asked patiently.

'I'm the managing director of a company which has just been taken over. Two weeks ago I was told that I would be offered a package which I know I can't refuse. Next Monday I am meeting a potential partner to discuss establishing a new internet-based company. His brother is called Robert and showed an interest in coming in with us. It looks as if I ought to say no. And it's true, as a young man I was made redundant and as a result founded the company which has just been bought out.' He stroked his nose pensively. 'How could you know all that from three ribbons?'

It seemed like a conjuring trick after all.

Hillary was non-plussed. She surveyed her group of students. 'Well,' she said again, 'now you've seen the demonstration, it's your turn.' Consternation thrilled through my veins. There was an excited (manic?) murmur amongst the students.

'There's nothing to worry about,' she carried on. 'All I want you to do is this.' She took a breath. 'First of all break into twos.' My neighbour and I looked sheepishly at each other, and with a mutual nod, agreed to be a two. 'In a moment I shall give each couple a set of ribbons.' Miniature versions of her ribbonned cards were distributed. 'Now, one of you hold the card while the other picks three colours they like.'

It was all too easy. 'Good,' she said like a primary school teacher. 'Now the card holder will look at the ribbons and just say whatever comes to mind. Don't try to think,' she warned us. 'Just go with the flow.'

The card was in my hand. Julia picked her three colours. It was time to go ..... with the flow?'

I looked at the three ribbons in my hand - cerise pink, sapphire blue and cream. My partner looked expectantly at me.

'Nice colours,' I said.

'Mm.'

I felt the satin between my finger tips and stroked it gently. 'I don't know what to say,' I apologised. 'Haven't a clue.' Hillary laid a hand on my shoulder and leaned over.

'So how are you getting on?' she asked gently.

'I'm sorry,' I said. 'I can't do this. I don't know where to start.'

'Of course you don't,' she said pleasantly. 'That's because you're thinking.'

'What else can I do?' Put me in charge and I'll organise anything I thought. But two minutes at this had reduced me to an inadequate. I didn't know whether to bark or cry.

'Don't think, just speak,' she suggested. 'Say the first thing that comes into your mind as you look at the ribbons.'

'They're very pretty,' I said lamely.

'That's good,' Hillary encouraged. (No it's not, I thought, it's completely inane.) 'But I suspect you are still thinking.' She looked at me directly. Her eyes were surprisingly blue, set off by her white hair. 'Now, how do you feel as you look at them? What feelings do they conjure up in you?' She egged me on.

'They're feminine, but strong. The blue in the middle is a strong colour. Not soft like the others.'

'That's Better!' she turned to Julia, my partner. (Be nice to me, I thought. It's your turn next.) 'Now, could you accept that you a caring and feminine person, but you are cool and strong in the centre?' Julia obligingly said yes to that. 'I expect you were born in October - Libra, right?'

'Well, yes!' she was more enthusiastic now.

'Right, what are you going to tell her next? You're doing fine,' my tutor said. She was certainly into positive reinforcement. I felt I was back at primary school and had just tied my first bow.

'You'd rather have a box of chocolates than a book as a present,' I said, more out of pique than anything else.

'That's very true.'

I decided to make it up as I went along. 'And you have a connection with Mozart. You're keen on classical music,' I added as my grand finale.

'I can't believe you said that,' said obliging Julia. 'I'm studying music and my assessment is a Mozart piece.'

'You are joking,' I said. 'Tell me you are joking.'

'I'm not joking,' her eyes danced with laughter.

'I think it has to be your turn.' I proffered her the ribbons as if I'd just discovered they were snakes. I'd forgotten Hillary was still behind me.

'Not bad!' she said as she fixed her gaze on her next wavering student across the room.

'Take your pick,' said Julia shaking out the ribbons once again. I chose sickly green, lilac and magenta. She surprised me by asking what I had done next. 'Just made it up as I went along. Just pretend it's an improvisation,' I suggested. We giggled like schoolgirls and I accepted my 'reading'. Amongst other things, she declared I had been through a difficult time but was growing through it. That I was sensitive (who would deny that?!). And that I was a powerful and flamboyant character when I chose to be. Well, it was good fun.

The first session took an hour and a half by the time we had exchanged readings and discussed our feedback. The aim, apparently, was to demonstrate that we all had basic psychic ability in some measure or other. If we were prepared to accept this, then we could use a range of techniques to strengthen or promote that ability.

The group stirred a little when, without thinking, I asked why we would want to 'promote' the ability. It was only then that I realised many of the people in the group were hoping to develop in order to give readings professionally or to gain insight into their lives. For some it wasn't fun at all - it was serious.

I suppose it was a mark of the progress I had made during the morning that I was now ready to see it as fun rather than character/ability assassination. But I could see I was marked out as a heretic by some.

'How did you get on?' I asked Iris back in the main conference area. She was in Jill's group. 'Great. We've been doing tarot,' she said.

'Pardon?'

'Just the Major Arcana though - the picture cards.'

'And what does the future hold Madame Iris?' We shared some chocolate.

'No, nothing like that. We just gave our impressions as we looked at the cards our partners chose.'

'Oh we used ribbons instead.' I explained the set up. 'So how intuitive were you?'

'I got a couple of things right,' as I offered her another bit of chocolate, 'more than I expected, but nothing earth-shattering.'

'How about Mozart for a music student?'

'That's not bad.' She looked around. 'What happens next, do you think?'

'The programme says a bit of theory before we go on to more practice after lunch.'

The workers were back on the platform, and Maggie, of the russet layers, began explaining that in our different ways, each group had given us the opportunity to realise that we each had some psychic ability. Assisted by John, using an overhead projector, she quoted examples of animals' psychic nature and followed that up with stories of mothers' intuition and the 'invisible link beyond friendship', as she called it.

In an earlier state before spoken and written language, she claimed, human beings were all psychic. They communicated telepathically rather like herd animals still do today. It was only with the coming of language that human beings were able to individualise and become separate entities in terms of their thought, she said. Ironically, instead of bringing people closer together in their awareness of each other, language cut them off from their natural 'communion' as she called it. Sometimes too, instead of making an idea clearer, language was and is used to confuse or cloud over the user's meaning. Sometimes on purpose, sometimes unintentionally.

This weekend's seminar was to explore and revive our ability to 'tune in' to other people and (in a sense) to go beyond language again and rebuild broken bridges.

I quite liked the idea of being more sensitive to other people, to become more responsive to them. I decided that was the tack I would take for the rest of the weekend. I didn't want to be psychic (in the sense I understood it) but I didn't mind being sensitive. It sounded better, and besides, it was in my colours, wasn't it? Being sensitive, I mean.

Just when you think it is safe .... I had just settled with this new position when Maggie spoiled it all by adding that people in the spirit world also used this psychic sense and communicated telepathically.

What people where? This wasn't on the programme. I fumbled for the last bit of chocolate only to find I had already eaten it.

CHAPTER 25

After lunch came chakras.

This time our group was led by John who explained that Hindu and Chinese philosophies (for example) recognised an energy system within the human body. Just as acupuncture identified meridians for chi energy throughout the body and manipulated those to restore physical and emotional well being, so these philosophies taught that there were spiritual centres chakras.

He showed us a diagram of a Buddha-like figure sitting crossed legged. Each of the chakras was represented by a colourful circle. Red at the base of the spine, orange beneath the tummy button, yellow at the stomach, green between the breasts, blue at the throat, indigo in the centre of the forehead and purple at the crown.

People jotted down notes while I admired the deftly drawn figure on the flip chart.

Everyone had these centres, he said, and they opened and closed rather like sea-anemones. When they were closed we would not be receptive to psychic impressions, but when they were open, we would be.

The purpose of his session was to teach us how to open and close these 'psychic centres' as he now called them. Pads, pens and clip boards were put down as he instructed people to sit easily in their straight-backed chairs. He would take them through a relaxation exercise, he said.

Directing our attention to our breathing, he asked us simply to become aware of it. I felt at home with that, as it startled me into realising how long it was since I practised according to Sybil's instructions.

'Now I want you to think about your feet,' he said, 'tense them up and then relax.' His exercise was a complete re-run of Sybil's! I was intrigued, but relaxed naturally and easily. Over the months the practice had become natural to me - like the talent for riding a bicycle (even if you don't do it very often). In the background, he played some soft music recorded over natural sounds of water and bird song. It would have been easy to nod off.

I was just on the verge of it when John's voice instructed us to envisage the base of our spines. 'Imagine a peony bud,' he said. 'Now think of gentle sunlight upon it. Let it blossom slowly and see the vivid scarlet petals unfold. Feel the energy as it flows through you.' I did as I was told and felt warm and comfortable.

'Move up your torso and this time imagine the bud of a marigold. As it opens to the warmth of the sun, it is vibrant orange, radiating energy.' I felt amused and cheerful as I unfolded.

'The next centre is at your stomach area,' John said helpfully. 'We'll have a sunflower here, only its centre will be as yellow as its petals. Open up gradually and feel the brightness spread right through your body,' he said. And it did - I was light and bright and cheerful. Enjoying myself.

'Think of your breast bone at this point,' he went on. 'As you do so, think of the green of fresh spring leaves with the sunlight shining through them. Let that green colour radiate from this centre. Feel its balance. Nothing is in conflict any more.' I went with his suggestion and all was well in my world. 'We shall move to the throat now,' he said after a minute or two. This time the bud there is a cornflower and as the warmth from the sunlight plays upon it, its petals unfurl astonishing royal blue. Breathe in that blue and feel its serenity. Become its serenity. It is beautiful,' he said. 'You are beautiful. Breathe it in.' The whole room seemed rapt in stillness.

'Go now to the centre of your forehead,' he instructed. 'And here let the purply blue of the iris flow gently to you and from you. Feel its softness, its gentleness. Here is the colour of knowing. Let it flow through you. Let it cleanse you of all wrong thinking. Bathe in its colour and feel compassion.' I was queen for the day, and gracious with it. I wanted to linger with this colour, but we moved inevitably on.

'Now you are at the top of your head - your crown. Let yourself open up here in the loving light of the sun. As you do so, become aware of rich, velvety purple of violets glow from you. Feel strong. Feel the power of inspiration and creativity that is the real you. Glow with the colour,' he said. I felt excitement with the edge of challenge I didn't think I was ready for purple. I realised I was taking these colours seriously, but decided to analyse it all later. I ventured further into purple.

'You are a raindrop....' he went on, 'capturing the light of the sun.... You are all colour and no colour.... You are transparent. ...You are a glint of white light.... Let the colour, let the light play around you.... Bathe in it dance with it, become it as you will.... Enjoy it....' He turned the background music up a little and left us to our experience for a while.

My world became a milky opal with glints and flashes of colour. Like a child in a garden, my attention was drawn first to fiery orange, then to lemon, pink and lime green. My mood changed as I looked. I became what I saw. I was delighted.

Then the tenor of the music altered and I simmered down. I wanted to pace gently, go carefully. I had danced through sunshine: now I wanted to stroll through clouds. Milky white, vaporous clouds. I felt dressed in drifting blue, but as I walked, the clouds became tinged with delicate pink and turned me to indigo. I flew in its skies and swam in its seas, breathing coloured air and sparkling with the pleasure of it all. Delight. Simple delight. When did I last feel this freedom?

Silent tears trickled slowly from my closed eyes. Washing pain away, dissolving the cramped restrictions of grief and convention and expectation. I felt relief.

'I think we're nearly all back now,' said a voice beyond the sky and the sea and the clouds. 'Just bring yourself back to your normal consciousness,' said the voice, 'back to this room with your friends and fellow students. Just bring yourself back and open your eyes when you feel ready.' The voice seemed closer now. 'Just when you feel ready, open your eyes and come back to yourself,' it said. 'Come back to yourself,' I jerked open my eyes to see John leaning over me slightly, talking to me, watching me.

'Are you all right now?' he asked gently. I looked to either side of me. People were watching quietly. I took a breath. 'Oh, yes. Sorry. I drifted off I think. I'm fine. I just need a hanky.' I dived into my bag as a diversion.

'That's OK then.' John made his way back to the front and asked the others for feedback while I came to terms with my experience.

CHAPTER 26

'We've been opening up. What have you been doing?' asked Iris as we met over coffee.

'The same thing, I think. Have you been using chakras and colour?' A lady in a long silk overshirt squeezed past us. 'Sorry,' she said and then looking more directly at me, added, 'oh, are you all right now? You must have gone very deep.'

'Yes, I'm fine now thanks. Just got a bit carried away,' and she disappeared into the crowd. Iris was intrigued. 'What have you been up to? We were just sensing energies and feeling our personal fields expand. Nothing deep.' She scrutinised me. I relayed my journey through colour, my emotional stint and my reluctance to come back .

'It's a whole new world, isn't it? Takes you to corners you never knew you had!' We took our cups back to the serving table. 'But are you sure you're all right now?' she was quite concerned. 'Yes,' I laughed. 'I'm feeling fine... I just had one of my corners cleared out. But you haven't told me about your session.'

'Well, Maggie talked to us about our personal energy field or aura. She said everyone had one, and we were to imagine the energy all around us and then expand it, which we did. A bit later on, she showed us how to see and feel that energy - I'll tell you more about that later - and then we extended our energy to other people and said what we felt. Do you know, I actually felt my partner's arthritis? I could actually tell which areas were sore. Honestly,' she bubbled on enthusiastically,' I've spent all day saying 'I don't believe this!' and yet it's right enough.' She stopped reluctantly for breath.

'So what are you going to do with all this amazement then?' I asked, like an old cynic.

'I'm going to follow it through and see where it takes me,' she said most determinedly. 'I want to know if this is an ability, and if so how it works, and whether it can change life for the better.'

'You're very serious,' I replied. 'You sound like a convert.'

'Not a convert, and investigator! Are you ready for the last session of the day?'

'Ready for almost anything.'

Maggie, Jill, Hillary and John had reassembled on the platform. 'In your various ways,' said Maggie, 'you have all been learning to 'open up' this afternoon, and in this last session your tutors are going to demonstrate how to work with psychometry. Once you've seen how it's done, you'll get the chance to experiment yourselves.' We settled back to be entertained for half an hour.

First of all, Jill came off the platform and circulated amongst the students with a tray, asking them for a small object which belonged to them. 'You'll get it back later,' she said. For a moment I thought we were going to play Kim's Game, like we did when we were children - guessing or remembering all the different objects on the tray. But no. Jill returned to the platform and placed the tray on a small table between Maggie and John.

Hillary stood up. 'We want to demonstrate to you that everyday objects hold vibrations, and that a trained psychic can read the object just by holding it. Sometimes the reader will give the history of the object, sometimes details about its owner.' She paused for effect. 'But because we want to show that we are reading the object and not you, please do not indicate that the object belongs to you until after the reading is completed. However,' she added with a smile, 'please do watch carefully to see which object has been chosen so that you don't miss anything if it does happen to belong to you!'

Maggie lifted a key fob and held it loosely in the palm of her hand. She closed her eyes for a moment and thought. Then she opened them and began her reading. 'I get a blue front door with this,' she said,' and a garden - quite small - with like cushions of flowers. There is a child - a toddler with a tricycle - a little boy with fair hair, and the name James. There's a cherry tree and I feel I'm in a fairly modern housing estate.' She paused. 'Who does this belong to?'

'It's mine,' said a blond haired woman in her fifties. 'I can take the blue door, the perennials and even the cherry tree. And we do live in an estate, but we don't have a child and James doesn't live in the house.'

Maggie was unperturbed. 'The people who lived in the house before you,' she said, 'they were quite young and they moved out of the neighbourhood.'

'Yes,' said the woman.

'Their toddler was killed on that estate,' she said. 'That's why they moved away.'

'I don't know,' came the reply.

'But if you ask your neighbours they'll be able to confirm that,' said Maggie. 'And your father's name was James.'

'Yes,' said the blond recipient.

'Fine,' said Maggie, still unperturbed. 'Now,' said Maggie to the audience, 'watch what John does.' John surveyed the tray, hesitating slightly before he picked up an enamelled pen.

'I'm drawn to this,' he said, rolling the pen between his fingertips.

'What do you mean 'drawn'?' interrogated Maggie.

'I mean I wanted to pick it up - as if I recognised it or felt comfortable with it.'

'OK. What are you doing with it now?' she was watching him.

'I'm just rolling it around and I'm watching to see what I feel or what thoughts come into my head.'

'And?'

'And I feel I want to write a letter, but I can't.'

'Why can't you?'

'Because the person I want to write to has gone away. I feel they died. I feel they gave me this pen as a present, but they died and I still miss them.' He went quiet as he gazed at the pen.

'So you're feeling like this other person is feeling?' Maggie interjected.

'Yes. It's like I become them for a little while.' He took us his reverie again. 'The pen is floral, so I suppose it belongs to a woman,' he went on.

'But that's your reasoning, nothing psychic,' Maggie interrupted again.

'Oh, right. Yes,' he said, but he went on, 'I feel she has fair hair. She has too much to do - family and children.'

'That's better!'

This time he ignored her. 'Too much sorting out to do. But she's getting there.'

'How do you know?'

'I feel positive about it.' He paused, 'She's determined. And she'll move. She'll live on the coast. She doesn't do that just now.'

'How do you know about the move?'

'I suddenly felt my whole world was being transported to fresher air. It was a good feeling. A feeling of freedom.'

'Well now,' said Maggie. 'Of course I wouldn't usually interrupt like that, but I wanted you to see what John was doing. He starts off with a quiet state of mind. Then he opens up, just like you were doing earlier, and then he gives an account of the impressions he is getting.'

She turned back to him as he laid the pen back down on the tray. 'Do you think about what you're saying, John? Do you analyse it?'

'No, Maggie, I just speak it out as if I were a translator at a conference - in the ear and out of the mouth, so to speak.'

'So there's no real effort involved?'

'The effort is in being alert to the impressions you get. But you don't try to generate the impressions. You just wait till they come.'

'So it's as easy as pie,' she concluded.

'Something like that! .... but you haven't checked it out with the owner yet.'

'Neither I have, but I'm just going to.' She lifted the pen from the tray. 'Whose is this?'

Iris' hand went up, 'Mine.'

'Just take us through the information then, dear,' Maggie invited, returning the pen to her. 'He was right about your fair hair. Tell us about the pen.'

86

'It was a present from my mother who died recently, and yes, I do miss her. There's been a lot of legal sorting out to do, but I don't feel I've too much to do.'

'But you have family?' Iris nodded. 'Then of course you have too much to do! Doesn't everyone?' Now the performer was emerging. Iris hardened up in response, 'And I will never live by the coast. I'm firmly established where I am.'

'But you do live in the city at present,' Maggie retaliated, 'and that's what counts.' She turned deftly from Iris and addressed the audience. 'Now, ladies and gentlemen, you can see how we work. It's not a bad showing for John, is it? And you are about to do just as well. First of all I'd like you to collect your objects from the tray.' There was a general rumble as people got out of their seats to retrieve their belongings.

When the hubbub died down, the instructions continued. 'Just move into groups of six, preferably with people you have not worked with so far today. Each put an object on the small tray Hillary will give you, and when you are ready, one by one, pick up an object and hold it loosely in your hand. Make a note of the first three impressions you receive. Give them off, and see if the owner can accept them....'

And so we whiled our time away until we stopped for dinner.

CHAPTER 27

Dinner was a buffet. The starters, fans of melon with a raspberry sauce and slices of kiwi fruit, were waiting for us on round tables set for six. Iris and I picked our places and sat down, waiting for another four to arrive. Gail, the lady in the silky overshirt, and her partner Bob sat next to us, followed by Hillary and a tall fair-haired man called Colin. After we exchanged names, we tucked in.

'Do you find you are able to eat before a demonstration?' Gail asked Hillary who was obviously relishing her meal.

She smiled, 'I'm not working tonight, so I can enjoy myself. To tell you the truth, I don't really like public demonstrations, I much prefer working one to one.' Her fork was poised over a juicy piece of melon. 'It's more comfortable, if you know what I mean.'

The evening session was described on the programme as 'an evening of clairvoyance'. I assumed that's what they were talking about.

'One-to-one, as you call it, makes a lot more sense to me,' Bob chipped in. 'I don't see the point in listening to other people's messages. I mean, what's in them for anyone else?'

Gail brushed her long hair to one side. 'I think it's interesting to see how evidential the mediumship can be. It's amazing sometimes to hear the fine detail a medium gives, and then to hear the recipient say yes, it's all correct. I mean, where could they have got the information from? They just couldn't have guessed all that, so it must be coming from people in spirit, like the medium says. Don't you find that interesting?' It was a challenge.

Bob finished his starter and put down his knife and fork determinedly. 'Most of the time I find it boring.' Gail flushed. 'How am I supposed to know of the medium's got it right? The recipient could be impressionable, or gullible, embarrassed to say no, or a plant, for all I know.'

'Bob, this is not the place...' she looked down, speaking under her breath.

'What I'm trying to say, is,' he turned more fully towards Gail who had pushed her plate away, 'I'm not knocking what Hillary does. I'm saying that mediumship is more meaningful one-to-one than it is as a public performance. As an experience, it should be subjective, not objective.'

'OK, OK,' she said, rising from the table, 'you're not with your college students now. Do you need to be so offensive?' She made her way to the buffet table and collected an empty plate. Bob shrugged his shoulders.

'Hillary, I'm not being offensive to you, am I?' He stretched back in his chair.

'Of course not dear,' she dabbed her lips with her napkin. 'I'm not that easily offended. I think in a sense you're both right. Objective makes you think; subjective makes you feel. You need both for the whole experience. That's why you and Gail need each other. Shall we join her at the buffet table?'

and with that she rose serenely to her feet without waiting for an answer. Bob strolled off in her wake.

'That,' said Colin, 'was cool.'

'Are you with them?' Iris nodded towards Gail and Bob.

'I've been in the same workshops as Bob today, but no. I'm on my own. Taking it all in,' he added with a grin. He was probably in his mid twenties and I wondered what his background was. He looked as if he could have been a student, but there was an edge about him, an extra sense of purpose. The three of us joined the queue for the buffet.

With piled plates, we returned to our table, wondering what round two would be like. Thankfully things were more relaxed, and for a while the food was our focus of attention. I hadn't realised how hungry I was.

I wondered to myself about Hillary. She seemed quite comfortable with the idea of her mediumship. What did she do? Did life seem different to her from her perspective? Could she read people's minds? She glanced over in my direction, but I decided that was just coincidence.

'What are you making of today, dear?' she asked me. I think she must call everyone dear. I paused mid-munch, trying to conjure up an appropriate answer. 'I imagine this is all rather unexpected, isn't it?' Why is she imagining things about me? Was I getting paranoid?

'Well, yes, it is.' She was just being the good hostess, drawing me into the conversation, I decided. 'I was persuaded to come along. I don't think I would have come on my own.'

'Join the club,' added Bob not too enigmatically.

'But now you're here,' she said, ignoring Bob, 'what do you think?'

'I think our minds and emotions are more powerful than I thought,' I said, surprising myself.

'But do you agree with the explanations?' It was Colin's question.

'What, psychic ability, chakras, auras?' He nodded. 'I don't know yet. Now, Iris here has declared herself an investigator of all of this, you should ask her. I'm just a beginner, a tourist even.'

'But the country's not so strange.' Hillary looked directly at me as she topped up my water. 'You're quite at home in this landscape. I'd say you were visiting friends,' she said, 'who normally come and visit you.' She put the jug down. 'But then, I'm allowed to be whimsical because I'm a medium!'

'That's a thing I wanted to ask you,' said Colin. 'Do you mind me asking you questions over dinner?'

'Carry on.'

'When they were introducing the team this morning, there were psychic consultants, a well known clairvoyant, and then they described you as a 'natural medium'. Why did they do that? Are the others unnatural, or what?'

'I've been a medium since I was a child. You know, seen things that weren't there, heard voices no one else did. So no one trained me or developed me.' She laughed,' I didn't attend seminars!' she said. 'The spirit world's been real to me all my life. No one told me about it. I lived in it.'

'What about the others?' said Iris.

'Well, to be fair, you would have to ask them.' She waved the question away with long, fine fingers.

'You don't call yourself a psychic,' Colin probed.

'That's right. I don't.' She looked directly back at him.

'All right then,' he laughed. 'Tell me, Hillary, why don't you describe yourself as a psychic? Why do you call yourself a medium instead?'

She allowed her fingers to interweave as she leant forward on the table. 'Partly because I'm awkward and old fashioned, and partly because I'm a pedant.'

'Go for it, Hillary!' Bob was on the verge of enthusiasm.

'Psychic refers to the faculty which perceives beyond the field of the five senses. A good psychic can tell you what your family is doing in Leeds when you're in Manchester. They can read your character from your eyes, your palms or your teacup - any focus will do. They have a beyond-average ability to perceive.'

'Then how is a medium different?' said Iris, hoping.

'A medium is psychic too. They have psychic ability, but they use it differently. You're heard of active and passive?'

'Pro-active and re-active is the latest jargon,' Bob again.

'I experience mediumship as the passive use of psychic ability - reactive,' she added for Bob. 'When I work as a medium, I don't intend to find something out. I don't aim for a particular contact. I stay receptive and wait for a communicator to use my quiet mind.'

'So you don't look for things to say, you wait to be told what to say,' Iris completed the idea.

'Yes. More or less. So that's the difference,' she said, turning to Colin with a smile.

'Who tells you what to say?'

'Either my spirit guide or a communicator from the spirit world.' She was obviously at ease with her answer.

'Dead people, you mean.'

'People whose bodies have died. Yes,' she corrected. 'In my experience they continue to live in spirit.'

'How can you be so sure?' Bob was stretched out, leaning back in his chair - too laid back to be laid back.

'Subjective experience matching objective experience.' Her eyes crinkled at the edges. 'But here's the sweet trolley, and sadly Maggie is calling me. Excuse me, won't you. Enjoy the rest of your meal.'

CHAPTER 28

The demonstration of clairvoyance, as it was billed, started at 7.30pm. The conference room had been straightened up since the afternoon, and further rows of chairs added. This evening, members of the public could pay to get in. As day students, our entry fee was half price.

Colin, who had been mingling with the large crowd, chatting to this one and that, came over to us prior to the start of the event.

'What do you expect to get out of this?' he asked us, focusing on Iris.

'Curiosity satisfied, perhaps an element of entertainment. If I'm lucky, perhaps a message.'

'Is there anyone in particular you would like to hear from?'

'My Mum died recently. That would be nice. But any message would give me some of Bob's 'subjective experience', wouldn't it? I'd be satisfied with that. It would be the first lead in my investigation!'

'Do any of the mediums know your Mum died recently?'

'I don't think so. I haven't told anyone. Have I?' She looked at me.

'This afternoon. In the psychometry, remember? John said your pen was a present from someone who had died ....'

'Oh yes. I'd forgotten about that. And in the feedback I explained about Mum.' She looked back at Colin. 'So they would all know.'

'So they would,' he said. 'If you don't mind me asking, do you want to believe that your mother still exists?'

'I'd like confirmation of what I already feel.'

'Would it make you feel better?'

'Yes, if you put it like that, it would.'

I felt a little edgy about all these questions, so I beat him to it as he turned to me.

'So why did you stay on this evening, Colin?'

'Me? I'm just looking for surprises,' he said.

And what will you do with them? I wondered.

As the seats filled, the background music became louder. It was the atmosphere of a theatre before curtain up. People found seats, waved to friends, struggled out of heavy coats. They opened up bags of sweets and chatted away. Reinforcing the effect, the main lights in the conference room were dimmed and those over the platform were brightened. There was a microphone centrally placed, and to one side, four chairs were set out behind a covered table with an elaborate flower arrangement on it.

There was a stirring and then a hush. Maggie, Jill and John walked down the side of the room, led by Hillary. Maggie and Jill were in dresses now, John in a suit with a Nheru jacket. They took their places behind the table

91

while Hillary stood centre stage at the microphone. When the background music faded, she formally welcomed the audience to the evening of clairvoyance, assuring them that with their love and support, this evening's sensitives would do their best to demonstrate the reality of life after death. At that, she introduced each of her colleagues.

Jill was the first to demonstrate.

'Right,' she said. 'Let's get down to business. Call me what you will - psychic, sensitive, medium, clairvoyant - my job this evening is to link you up with friends, relatives and acquaintances from the other side of life. People who have died, but who live on in the next life.' She paused for effect and looked around her audience. 'Sometimes I'll describe them. Sometimes give a name. Other times I'll go over something which happened in the past, or give you their guidance for the future. But we need to do a deal, you and I. If I speak to you, you've got to speak back to me. No response, no message. That's the deal.' Again she paused. 'These people have made quite an effort to communicate with you through me this evening. The least you can do is speak back to them, I think you'll agree.' She smoothed down her dress.

'And another thing, before I begin,' she said. 'I don't call up these people. I don't try to get you anyone you want. I just tell you who I'm aware of, so please don't say no to me just because you haven't got the person you're looking for.' She looked down, as if concentrating or listening to something. The audience was silent and attentive.

I wasn't expecting this kind of approach at all. She didn't pray. She wasn't holy. She wasn't respectful of these people 'from the other side of life' as she put it, or in awe of them. Rather she sounded more like an old fashioned telephonist linking one caller with another.

If this is what it's supposed to be, I thought to myself, I should be astounded. Dead people speaking to us just like their old selves. Why am I not amazed? Where's the media? How long has this sort of thing been going on for anyway? Why haven't I heard of it before? There was a snowstorm of questions bursting in my head. I fidgeted in my seat and then tried to settle down again.

Jill was addressing her audience again. 'I don't know exactly who I'm going to,' she said, 'but I want someone who can recognise a lady who would have liked Japanese things. She would have owned two Japanese vases that would have sat on a mantelpiece in her home. She was small, slim, dark hair whiter at the sides before she died. Little beady eyes. This lady lived in a terraced house and would have been in her seventies when she passed.' Two or three people raised their hands as recognising the character. 'These vases would have been given to her by a brother who had been in the navy. He is also in spirit now.' The three hands reduced to one. 'Then it looks as if I'm with you - the lady in blue,' she said to the recipient. One of the girls from the stall moved towards her with a microphone. 'Can you accept this lady?' Jill continued.

'I think so,' came the reply.

'This lady feels like an aunt on your father's side of the family. Is that possible?'

'Yes, but I didn't know her very well.'

'That's all right, but you remember the terraced house and the two vases?'

'Yes.'

'And the uncle at sea?'

'I never met him, but I think so.'

It was interesting, but a bit vague. Why didn't they just say it's your Auntie Peggy here? I supposed it couldn't be a straightforward as that.

'I have the name Edna,' Jill continued.

'That's another aunt.'

'She's in spirit too.'

'Yes.'

'Her husband liked growing runner beans, and she's laughing here. She's saying you've started a project and it isn't growing fast enough for your liking.' No response. 'Is that true?'

'Yes it could be.'

'She's saying you hoped it would build up quicker and bring in some money soon. She's saying you never had much patience, and it's time you learned it now. Was she very blunt this lady?'

'Yes.'

'Well, she's just come to say hold on. Don't give up on this project. Another six months will see better returns if you just stay with it. And she sends her love.'

'Thank you.' The sitter seemed relatively pleased with this, but I was pulled two ways. Part of me wanted to ask - Is that it then? You live a life and then come back to talk about vases and runner beans. I somehow thought messages would be more important, loftier, wiser perhaps. But then I asked myself how many lofty conversations I had over the phone with friends - not many! On the other hand, the information seemed such a miscellaneous batch and yet the recipient could accept it. If Jill had come to me, I couldn't have accepted that.

I continued to ponder in this way as one message followed another. Generally they took about five minutes each. Some were more specific than others. Occasionally someone would be given a guide or spirit helper, whatever that was. I continued to listen and noticed that Colin jotted down things from time to time.

After half an hour or so, it was John's turn. He stood up and paced nervously back and forth on the platform. Then he paused and seemed to search the audience.

'Oh, there you are,' he said. 'The lady left of centre. You're wearing a slate grey fleece, I think.'

'Me?' said Iris, pointing at herself.

'Yes. I believe I worked with you earlier today.' The microphone was pushed into her hand. It disconcerted her.

'Er, yes. That's right,' she said.

'I believe I have your mother here,' he said quite assertively. 'This woman gives me initials M and J. They are her initials, are they not?'

'Mm,' Iris mumbled.

'Pardon?'

'Yes, that's right.'

'She tells me that before her passing she was unwell, made a recovery and then passed suddenly.'

'Yes.'

'In hospital, and you were there at the time.'

'I was.' I felt panicked by this and could feel my heart thumping. Goodness knows how Iris was feeling. She looked perfectly composed.

'She tells me your friend was with you at the hospital. She's here with you tonight.' I didn't know whether to laugh or cry. 'She says thank you for the flowers and the fireworks ... what can she mean by that? It doesn't make sense to me.'

'I know what she means,' said Iris, this time with tears in her eyes as we looked at each other.

'I have to tell you from her to keep investigating, but not to believe everything you see and hear. And air. What's this about air? A breath of fresh air will be good for you, she says. There's a gentleman with her - her husband I think. They're both laughing and sending their love. Is this a joke, do you think?'

'I don't know,' said Iris.

'Well, will you watch out for it? And you must have children,' he said. 'She's telling you to give them a hug 'from both of us'. Will you do that?'

'Yes,' sniffed Iris as I groped about my bag for another tissue.

'That will be fine,' John concluded, and launched onto his next link.

The rest of the performance washed over me. I squeezed Iris's hand in mutual support and tried to gaze at the platform as if I was totally nonplussed. It was as if someone had told me a whole new continent had just been discovered. I was a battleground of disbelief and anticipation.

94

As the crowd poured out into the cold, March, evening air, I turned to Iris to see how she was doing. 'Are you all right?'

'Yes. I'm fine. I'm just so glad you came with me today,' she said. Her eyes were bright. 'Of course the whole thing's been good fun, but this evening you were there with me. Hearing what I heard. Confirming it. It's just so reassuring somehow.' We linked arms as we walked back to the car park. 'It'll be so much easier to get on with life now,' she added as the car doors unlocked. ' No more looking back. I can look forward.' The door closed with a thump as she turned on the ignition. 'And I can think a thought to Mum whenever I feel like it!'

'What was the MJ, anyway?' I asked as we zoomed off onto the motorway.

'Marjorie Jean.'

'I never knew that! And what about the fresh air?'

'Now, I haven't a clue about that,' she admitted. 'Maybe it'll come to me later. Or maybe it hasn't happened yet.' she concentrated on her driving.

'Do you really believe that?' I asked. 'Predictions. That a medium could tell you what will happen next?' Iris indicated to turn off the motorway and on to a local road. Left again and we were into a residential area.

'I don't know what I think,' she said, swinging into a street I recognised from early this morning. 'But if something about fresh air happens, then yes, I'll believe it.' We were in her driveway now, with the light from the pre-set lamps shining through the glass of the front door and the lounge. 'Isn't it quiet?' she said, opening the door. 'No kids, no Rumble, no Peter!' We crept in in case an ambush was in store for us. 'I'll put the kettle on and then give them a ring. Do you fancy some toast?' I nodded and then shrugged my coat off and went to turn on the fire in the lounge and pull the curtains fully closed. As I sank back in a cosy chair, I could hear her chatting on the phone in the hall. 'We've had a magical day!' I heard her saying. 'Wait till I get you home and I'll tell you all about it. How are the kids? ... Did you survive the Nature Trail? .... And how about the fishing?....Not a video! ....' It sounded as if all was well with the happy campers.

She came through with a tray of tea, toast and a variety of spreads. 'Help yourself,' she said, handing me a knife and a plate. 'Would you believe their fishing was rained off this afternoon? Some fishermen, eh! So they bought fish and chips and watched a video someone had left at the cottage. Now they're on to card games.'

'You mean strip poker, that kind of thing?' I buttered my toast indulgently.

'Well, whatever it is, they sound as if they're having a fine time.' Iris wrapped herself round her mug of tea and pushed her hair out of her eyes. 'I don't know about you, but I'm just about wiped out. Do you think we've got the stamina for tomorrow?'

'We've paid for it, haven't we?' she nodded. 'Then of course we've got the stamina for it!' I stretched out in front of the fire, dangerously near to sleep. 'Let's see the programme anyway, till we see what's on offer.' Iris hauled her bag over towards her and produced the weekend's programme. Finishing a half slice of toast, she wiped her fingers on her sweatshirt, grinned up at me, and started reading.

'Ten till five,' she announced. 'There will be four main groups 'that students will self-select'. Namely: Introduction to Tarot, Exercising Extra Sensory Perception, Awareness of Spirit and Sensitivity through Colour. What do you fancy?' she looked over the top of the programme at me.

'Who's doing what?'

'Ah, now. Let me see,' she went back to scrutinising the programme. 'Jill's on Tarot, Maggie on ESP, Hillary on Awareness and John on Colour.'

'Hillary or John, I think.'

'You mean you're choosing by personality, not subject?'

'Well,' I wriggled my toes in front of the fire, 'I'm going to be with them all day, so I'm better to like them. What about you?'

'I fancy the ESP. But then again, you got a lot out of that colour session, didn't you? Don't you fancy taking that further? I might like that.'

'But then again, Hillary's real ...'

'You mean the rest aren't? John was pretty impressive.'

'I don't mean that. No, I admire the way he worked. It's just that Hillary seems to have her feet on the ground. You might go to her if you had a problem. I don't think I'd go to the others. Would you?'

'They're not meant to be agony aunts, are they?' she curled up in the corner of the settee. 'But I know what you mean. They're more like stage personalities. What did you make of her comment about visiting friends?'

'Whose?'

'Hillary's. To you, over dinner.'

'I'd forgotten about that. That's when she said she was allowed to be whimsical, wasn't it?'

'Yes, you said you felt like a tourist and she said it was more as if you were visiting friends who usually came to you, or something.'

'It's as if she gets inside you when you least expect it.' I emptied my mug and put it back on the tray.

'What do you mean? Did she strike a chord?'

'It's hard to say, really. There have been times on and off when I've found myself having a conversation in my head. You know - in quiet moments. Except sometimes I've wondered if I was really talking to myself, or whether I was talking to someone else.'

'Wouldn't you know the difference?' she pushed the hair out of her eyes again.

'You'd think you would, wouldn't you? But sometimes the answers surprised me, or the conclusions were unexpected. And then I wondered if it was me.'

'Who else could it be?'

'Well, that's the obvious question, isn't it? And up until today, my obvious answer was that it couldn't possibly be anyone else. Now Hillary's made me wonder. And John, tonight, made me wonder further.' I gazed at the fire for a moment, watching the reflector move with the heat, generating little flames in the background. 'If the figure in my mind came to me, so to speak, maybe by coming here and discovering a world of spirit or whatever, I've sort of come to them.'

Iris looked surprised. Her tiredness left her. 'You've never told me this before!'

'I've spoken a little to Mhairi about it, and Tom,' I said apologetically, 'but if you think it's a kind of madness, you're inclined to keep quiet about it, don't you think?'

'But who are you talking to and what are they saying? Tell me!'

This must be what coming out feels like, I thought to myself. I would have preferred not to do it.

'I nicknamed her Sybil,' I said rather foolishly. 'And we've talked about meditation, self awareness, that sort of thing. Nothing very remarkable.... But I must admit I enjoy talking to her, although we have fallen out occasionally.'

Iris laughed. 'What's she like? Where did she come from?' She waited, like a child waiting to hear a bedtime story.

'Oh, Iris, I don't know. She's just Sybil. Her appearance changes from time to time, but it's more or less ordinary. I don't know her history - or even if she's got one!'

'But you do talk to her, so she must have some credibility. How long has she been around.'

'About two years, I suppose.'

'Huh! You're incredible!'

'She taught me how to give healing when your Mum wasn't well, but I was so upset that I couldn't save her that I gave up on Sybil for a while. We're back on speaking terms now, but I'm very cautious.'

'Oh, another thing for me to investigate! I'm fascinated.... '

'But not tonight, you're wiped out, remember?'

'OK then. But one last thing, who shall we go to tomorrow, Hillary?'

'John.'

'You mean you're opting for the quiet life?' she teased.

'Yes. Something like that.'

It seemed like no time until we were back at the hotel, milling around the stalls, coffee in hand. This time the faces were more familiar and I'd stopped trying to look enigmatic. I still didn't want to buy an account of past lives or to unlock my potential with inspirational cards, but White Eagle's 'The Quiet Mind' or 'The Teachings of Silver Birch' held their own charm ... perhaps later.

There was no formal welcome session today. We were just going to get straight to work, said the notice board which offered the list of options with room numbers against them. The Colour group was room four. Finally Iris plumped for exercising her ESP with Maggie in Room 2. It was more investigatable, she said.

People began milling towards their rooms.

'May the Power be with you!' I said to Iris just as she was leaving. 'I think I'll just pop to the loo first.' Unknown to me, Flower Arrangers International were meeting in the larger conference suite next to ours, and unfortunately every second one of them had the same call of nature to obey as I had. The queue was everlasting. I finally scuttled off to Room Four and slipped discretely in, to sit at the back.

Hillary was in charge, and in the midst of pairing people off for an exercise she was going to do later.

'Oh, I'm sorry,' I said, 'I thought this was the Colour group.'

'It was, until John decided the natural light was better in Room Three. We swapped,' said Hillary pleasantly, ' but don't go. We're one short. We need you.' Bob lingered by her side, looking lost and partnerless. It would have been churlish to go.

'Just think of it as fate,' he said as I approached.

'How's Gail today?' I retorted.

'Indulging in colour.' I sat down and awaited my instructions.

'We can't begin to explore our sensitivity to spirit until we understand the basics of energy,' she said. 'So we're going to start with ourselves.' She looked round the group, watching their expressions. 'I'm not going to give you any fancy terminology. Today we're dealing in plain English and practical experience. But your day shouldn't be any the less informative for that.' she added.

'Now,' she went on, 'I expect you remember the meditative state you were practising yesterday. I want you to slip back into that just now. Sit well back in your chairs. Imagine a little flame glowing softly at the heart of you. As you breathe in, let the flame glow more brightly. As you breathe out, let it grow bigger. Breathe in and brighten. Breathe out and extend. In to brighten, out to extend,' she repeated.

'Imagine now that your flame has extended so much that it surrounds you in its light. You are seated in the middle of the light, and it infuses your body with energy. You can feel yourself tingling with that energy,' she insisted. 'Just sit there and feel it.' I allowed myself to imagine the feeling.

'That's good,' she said again. 'Now when you feel ready, please open your eyes and become aware of your fellow students in the room. Stay relaxed, but open your eyes.' We did. Then she surprised us with her next instruction. 'Rub your hands briskly together,' she said, 'as if it was a really cold morning. Go on, rub hard!' Again we did as we were told. 'Now bring the palms of your hands close together as if your were about to pray,' she said,' and just as you are about to bring them fully together let your hands drift apart just as much as you want them to.' Most of us found our hands drifting about thirty to forty centimetres apart. 'Keep your attention on the feeling between your palms. You find your hands at a comfortable distance apart. Slowly begin to draw them in. What do you feel as you do this? Let them go out again. Now. What are you feeling?' She looked around and smiled at us. 'It's like holding a soft balloon between your palms,' said Julia, my partner from yesterday morning. ' It pushes the hands out a little as you press in,' she laughed lightly in her amusement. I could feel what she meant. One or two others murmured their agreement. We sat around as if playing imaginary concertinas. I laughed at the daftness of it.

'What you are feeling,' said Hillary, 'is your own energy. Your physical body is surrounded by an energy field which we're going to call the aura. I have encouraged you through meditation to 'open up' and extend this field. When you train yourself to see it, you will realise that it follows your movements almost like a cloud. It swirls softly around you. But just now you are simply experiencing its existence through touch. The 'cloud' from one hand is simply bouncing off the other. That's what you are feeling.' We stopped concertina-ing.

'Now let's try something else!' We watched for her next movement. 'Ideally you want to do this against a plain background. Black's best. However, do this!' She splayed both hands in front of her, palms down, middle fingers touching. OK?' With her head down, she looked at us from under her eyebrows. 'Now gently draw your hands apart. What do you see?'

'Smoke!' said a broad built man incredulously.

'Oh yes, so it is, Gerrard!' his neighbour chipped in. 'Pale drifts of smoke. I can see it too!'

'Can the rest of you see that?' Hillary enquired. There was a rumble of agreement. 'Then move your right hand diagonally away from your left. Slowly now. What do you see?'

'The smoke moves diagonally too and then breaks off,' Gerrard commented as unelected group spokesman.

'Move your hands closer again. What's going on now?'

'It joins up again.'

'Yes. It's energy flowing from one fingertip to another. Your energy. And when the gap is too wide, the flow breaks off. I'm glad you came!' Hillary joked with him.

She stood fully upright again and looked full at us. 'So now you have not only felt the energy around you, you have caught a glimpse of it.'

'I didn't,' said Bob.

'Well, when you've time, try again in a softly lit room when you're feeling relaxed. You need to look lazily. Don't focus too hard. Don't concentrate. Just gaze softly. The worst thing to do is to get uptight about it,' she added, 'although I can see you're not uptight, of course.'

'I haven't forgotten I got you all partnered up earlier,' she said to the group. 'We're going to work in twos shortly, but before we do that, I want to put you in groups of eight or ten. Would you do that for me please? Just draw your chairs into a circle formation. Eight to ten people will be fine.' Once again we shuffled about into the required circle.

'Keep about six inches between you.' She walked round the room, inspecting.

'Go back to that meditative state again, will you? And let that light radiate out from you. That's good. Now, extend your light to the right of you. Just let it dwell on the person to your right. Stay relaxed. Now accept the first impressions that come to mind. OK. And remember them if you can.' I felt a busy energy, restless, relentless. Then I remembered Bob was sitting to my right.

'Draw your attention away from that direction and extend your light and your energy to the left of you. Do the same as before. What do you feel now?' I felt pain right down my spine. I felt brittle and fragile. Hillary brought us back to ourselves and instructed us to tell our neighbours what we sensed.

I relayed my impressions to Bob who smiled laconically and said, 'That figures, but then you knew I was sitting next to you, didn't you?'

'Of course.'

'I sensed a bossiness with you. Capable but quiet.'

'I'll accept that, but ...'

'I knew I was sitting next to you!' he finished the sentence.

The lady to my left didn't sense anything, she said, except a warmth. 'Do you do healing?' she asked.

'I don't really know,' I said, not wanting to defy the Trades Descriptions Act, 'but are you having problems with your back? I felt pain with you, right down the spine, as if it was very fragile.' She smiled wanely at me. 'I'm going to hospital for tests on it next week.' I nearly said, 'Oh good!' because my impression was right, but restrained myself just in time and offered sympathy instead.

Before Hillary rounded off the session, it appeared as if our impressions were generally more right than wrong. Bob rephrased that as impressions were more rightly general than wrong. 'I'm glad you're here, for balance!' was Hillary's response to that.

Using the same format, as the last part of the session, we 'tuned in' once more and sensed the energy in our circle. I could feel it pulsing. I felt comfortable and supported within it. In fact I didn't want to 'leave' it when we were asked to draw our energies back to ourselves. It was a curious sensation.

'So often I am asked why trainee mediums sit in circle,' said Hillary at the end of the exercise. 'Yet the answer is so simple. It's for the answers you have just been giving me. It is energising, it is supportive, uplifting. It acts a bit like a satellite dish in that it intensifies the signal. Your circle of energy is exactly that. It bumps up the signal from spirit communicators until you, as the budding medium, learn to pick up more subtle signals. It's all common sense really,' she said before she stopped to take questions.

CHAPTER 31

'What has energy got to do with spirit communication?' It was Colin. I hadn't realised he was in this group.

'Before I answer that, let me ask you a question,' said Hillary.

'OK.' He had his notepad at the ready.

'What do you think people in spirit are like?'

'Just like they were when they were alive and here.'

'Do you mean that they will be just as physical?'

'No, I suppose they have shed the physical part of them. I thought you were talking about their personalities,' he replied.

'No. I wanted to know what they would be made of if they were no longer physical stuff.'

'Something that can walk through walls, I suppose!'

'So you think they must still have some sort of form?'

'Well, if they didn't have a form, how would I recognise them?'

She came back with, 'You tell me.'

'Well if they didn't have an exact form (like a physical body), perhaps they would have an energy field, or an energy pattern. Something that could be picked up and translated back into what I think of as a physical form.... Like a radio station transforms sound into radio waves, transmits them, and my radio converts the waves back into sound so that I can hear it again.'

'And radio waves can go through walls, can't they?' Hillary added.

'Yes.'

'Well done. You've answered your own question, and probably better than I could have done.'

Colin looked at her in disbelief. 'Are you saying that when people die, they remain as an energy field - a bundle of energy?'

'A conscious energy field. Yes. An energy which can think and will and remember and feel emotion and create.... and love. I would describe spirit people that way.'

'But how can you love an energy field?' asked Julia.

'You already do,' said Hillary, 'only there's a physical body at the centre of it.'

'Well what's at the centre of it once the physical body is gone?' asked someone behind me, 'or will we be like polo mints with holes in the middle?'

'The Theosophists explain it quite well diagrammatically,' she replied. 'They describe the next centre as the astral body. At present, your life or your reality is bounded and determined by the physical; after the death of the physical, your life is determined instead by the emotional.'

'If that's true, it could be pretty tempestuous and unpredictable,' said Bob.

'Yes. It could, couldn't it?' She smiled a little.

'And do you cast off the astral body eventually?' the same enquirer asked.

'I believe so. You work your way from that through the lower and higher mental bodies, on to the causal and the celestial or soul body. Goodness knows what happens after that!'

'What evidence is there for all this?' Colin went on.

'Well, it forms the basis of many traditional Eastern teachings - Suffism, Islam, Zoroastrianism and so on. That's not evidence, I admit, but each is a cultural precursor. It is not a new idea. It was just repackaged for the West by Theosophy at the turn of the nineteenth century and has found its way into New Age thought since then.

'Evidence comes in other ways, I think. Where spirit communicators have been asked about their lives 'on the other side', many initial descriptions are parallel to the kind of experience you and I have here. That's natural, I suppose. Evolving life rarely makes radical shifts. Change tends to occur in a series of stages. Be that as it may, later accounts of life in the spirit world refer to people thinking about a place and suddenly being there (as if there were no requirement to travel through a physical landscape or cover physical distance). Such spirit people tell us they feel our emotions of both grief and joy much more intensely, and that these feelings colour (or influence) their surroundings to a significant extent.

'These kind of descriptions come from sources from a wide variety of times and cultures. Their consistency encourages us to consider them as evidence. I'll give you a list of authors if you are interested,' she said to Colin who was still jotting away.

'But some people would claim they have had direct experience of such states of being. If you care to read up on astral travel, then again you will find sketches of what life in spirit might be like, bearing in mind that they are expressed in our language, not theirs.'

'What do you mean by that?' I asked.

'The language we speak here has evolved in a physical environment, through a physical vehicle and is designed to convey the experience of life in a physical dimension. Life in a different dimension will be a different experience, won't it?' I nodded uncertainly, 'and would therefore require a different (or extended) language.' I must have looked puzzled.

'Imagine you could communicate with a fish,' she said, taking me painfully slowly through the idea. 'How would you communicate the idea of frost to a fish? It's beyond his life experience. Worse still, how could you convey the notion of the combustion engine? It is central to the way we live, and yet has no role in his life. Describing it to him would be meaningless. The

103

same must be true of a life unbounded by physical restriction, a life powered by emotion or thought. Do you see?' I thought I did.

'Does that explain why many messages from people in spirit are so, well, mundane?' asked Julia.

'It could do. But that might also be due to the limitations of the medium or the low expectations of the sitter. However.....,' she paused for a moment. 'I think we're trying to run the marathon before we've learned to walk. Let's put this in perspective. So far, you've learned how to become aware of the energy around you. You've felt the difference between the absence and presence of an individual's energy. That's all you've done. Don't analyse mediumship out of existence before you've even experienced it. And don't,' she said, looking rather pointedly at one or two of us, 'expect to experience mediumship at the snap of a finger. With most people, it's an awareness that develops gradually. With many people,' she went on, 'it develops without them sitting in developing circles or being taught by people like me.'

'So how does it develop with them?' Colin asked.

'Through their religious practice.'

'Meaning?' It was apparent Bob wasn't too keen on religious references.

'Meaning prayer, contemplation, service, meditation, reflection, 'good works' even. Any effort that you put in to being at one with a higher power.'

'Then why aren't there mediums everywhere?'

'Some people prefer not to talk about their expanded awareness. Their gift may only be spasmodic. Or they may choose to describe it as insight. Or, quite simply, they may not want to draw attention to themselves.'

'Would you describe yourself then as an attention seeker?' asked Colin with a grin, pen still in hand.

'Definitely!' Hillary was quite emphatic and Colin looked taken aback. 'I seek attention for the spiritual aspect of life. People have forgotten it in the rush. If my mediumship, or yours,' she added as a challenge, 'startles people into thinking about the deeper aspects of themselves, then I'll be happy with that.' He stopped writing.

'Won't that fit into your article somewhere?' she raised an eyebrow.

'I didn't tell you I...'

'You didn't need to. You've been interviewing me for the past twenty minutes. Just as you were at dinner last night. And I don't need to be psychic to work that out.' There was a watchful pause. Hillary seemed quite at ease with the situation. 'I think we'll resume after coffee,' she said and ended the session there.

CHAPTER 32

'Which newspaper are we all going to be famous in?' Bob asked as Hillary left us to our own devices.

'I'm freelance. Perhaps one of the Sunday supplements, if I'm lucky.'

'You're a mole, a spy!' Bob was enjoying the melodrama.

'Not at all. I'm as curious and uncommitted as you are. But there's some good material here. She's not what I expected her to be.'

'It's not her we're concerned about,' said Bob, suddenly including the gathering group in his newly created concern. 'It's us. What are you going to say about us?'

'Oh....., "Leading Sociology Lecturer Links up with the Astral. - In his researches into the higher levels of esoteric societies, Bob Stanwell, author of the soon-to-be-published book on 'The Norms and Mores of the New Labour Society', applied his newly found abilities to read subtle energies and stepped into the whole new society of the life beyond death....'

I like to think I saw Bob pale at the thought.

'How'm I doing?'

'You're winding him up beautifully,' said Julia as she handed Bob a carton coffee. 'Are you really going to write a piece?'

'Well, if I do, rest assured Bob, it's more likely to be about Hillary and her colleagues. You don't mind not being the star, do you?'

'I think I could live with that,' said a much relieved author.

I made my way over to the coffee table where Iris was queuing.

'How's colour with John, then?'

'I'm in the wrong group,' I said. 'They swapped rooms before I got there, so I'm with Hillary after all!'

'It must have been meant,' she said.

'You're beginning to sound like everyone else round here .... everything's part of The Plan.' She handed me a coffee.

'I bet you it is, though!' Now it was me who was being wound up. 'You're enjoying it, aren't you?'

'After the initial shock. yes, I suppose I am,' I said grudgingly.

'Wow! There's enthusiasm for you! So have you had any messages yet, or given any?'

'No. We've been sensing energies and talking about the nature of people in spirit. We haven't got to messages yet. But we have discovered that Colin's a journalist. Bob nearly freaked when he thought he might get a spooky write up. But I think he's beginning to recover .... now that he knows he's not going to be the centre of the piece!'

'I thought he asked a lot of questions. Do you think he's got colleagues in the other groups?'

'Haven't a clue, but you could always ask him. Anyway, how's ESP? It's nearly time for us to go back in.'

'It's fun. We've been using Zener cards to measure our powers of telepathy. We have to write down the symbol the 'sender' is thinking of.'

'And ...?'

'And I scored eight hits out of a possible twenty five. The average score is five, so who knows, I may have some positive potential here! We're off to do the Ganzfeld procedure now, whatever that is!' Back to 'work' we went.

When we returned to our room, the chairs were set out in one large circle. We took our seats quickly and quietly and looked again to Hillary who remained standing.

'Right. Everyone comfortable? If you have heavy jackets, bags or other clutter, I'm going to ask you to put them to the side of the room out of the way. I want you to feel you are uncluttered and are comfortable in your own space.' A few of us moved around and de-cluttered.

'If you think you might want some water to sip, come and get a glass now and put it beside you so that it's there when you need it.' Again, a few people moved. The room was pleasant and softly lit. Daylight came through the windows set high in the walls, and little spotlights in the ceiling contributed to the gentle lighting effect. We sat back comfortably, and waited.

'In this session, I'm going to teach you how to set up a group for developing your awareness. In the old days, this was often called circle work for obvious reasons - you're sitting in a circle! From what you've said, very few of you have sat for development before, so I'm going to start from the beginning and assume you know nothing. OK?' Colin reached for his pad once more.

'You won't need that,' smiled Hillary. 'I want you to participate fully in what we are doing in the group, so I've made you a handout to cover the main instructions. All you need to do is listen.' Her voice was reassuring, but not hypnotic.

'Here we go, then,' she said. 'You'll be good at this by now, because the first thing I want you to do is to close your eyes, relax, listen to your breathing and still your mind.' She took us through the familiar procedure step by step.

'Now I like to say a prayer before I begin to work. If you are not religiously inclined, that's fine. Choose a little inspiring poetry or repeat a positive affirmation at the start. The important thing is to tell your self you are working with all that is good and beautiful and true; and that you are doing it for the benefit of everyone. In a sense, your statement or prayer sets the tone of your work.' She was silent for a moment or two, until she made her prayer.

106

'Great Spirit, Father God, we come into your presence now as your children. We seek your love and your understanding. Let our souls open to your presence now. Let us feel your gentle care. Let us feel your powerful wisdom. Fill us Father with awareness of your presence.....' A feeling of peace slipped silently into the atmosphere. I felt reassured and expectant at the same time. '.... And where our friends in spirit wish to draw close to touch our awareness, let it be so Father, in your name of love. Amen.' There was a murmur of 'amen' around the circle.

'At this point, imagine the light within you once more, like you did this morning,' she encouraged. 'Brighten that light as you breathe in and expand the light as you breathe out.' She repeated the instructions as she encouraged us to 'expand'.

'Good.' The voice was liquid and soothing. 'Keep going .... you can feel the energy around you. Feel that beautiful energy as it moves and pulses round the circle.' I found myself warm and happy in light again, like sitting in sunshine on a good summer's day.

'Now, just keep your eyes closed and maintain your relaxed state of mind,' the voice continued. 'There's a blank screen inside your head. Stay watchful and see what comes...... For the next five minutes or so, I shall let soft music play gently in the background,' she faded in the music, 'and I want you to do nothing more than watch. Watch the screen and watch what you are feeling..... Go with it.'

The music played, but I was only barely conscious of it. Its rhythm painted colours on my screen. They would appear, melt and blend into another colour, and another - pale green, turquoise, sand gold and warm tangerine. I watched idyllic scenes mix with snapshots of memories, glimpses of faces, flickers of old feelings. Sybil came and went, proffering an artist's palette and a bunch of brushes. I watched it all happen.

As the music faded completely, Hillary's voice returned. 'Stay nice and relaxed,' she said, 'and when you feel ready, open your eyes and look round the circle. Feel at home here.'

After checking that we were all comfortable, she continued. 'In normal circumstances in a development group, you might well sit in that watchful condition for half an hour or so, without any interruption. But because this is a training group, I'm butting in at this point to explain what we're doing, and to help you along a bit. So here you are. You are sitting in a circle of energy. You are watching for impressions which are more likely to be noticeable because of the energy. And what do you see?' She looked around the group, 'Colin?'

'Em, well, nothing really. Nothing.'

'Exactly! Nearly everyone says that at first. And they are quite right. Did you see nothing too?' she turned to Julia on her left.

'Yes,' said Julia, relieved that the question wasn't more demanding. 'Just a few colours. That's all.'

'Tell me,' Hillary leaned towards her a little. 'What did you expect to see?'

'Well, a figure perhaps. Or a face. Or maybe an object.'

'And you didn't see those things?'

'No. Not at all.'

'So you saw nothing?'

'That's right.'

'Except colour. .... Is colour nothing?'

'Nothing specific, if you know what I mean,' said Julia.

'So what you're saying is, you didn't see what you expected to see, but you did see something - colour.'

'Yes, that's a more accurate description.'

'I'm glad you're here,' said Hillary, ' you and Colin, that is. Because you've demonstrated beautifully the problem most people have with developing awareness..'

'What's that?' asked Colin.

'You deny your experience because it is not what you expect. In a sense you are blind to it, like the aborigines were blind to the masts on Captain Cook's ships. They had never seen sail boats before, and because they didn't expect to see masts, they didn't see them, and they couldn't work out how the boats moved without oars. ... If you come into development expecting it to be a certain way, and things don't happen the way you expect, then you'll think nothing is happening at all. And you'll be wrong!' Hillary was enjoying herself.

CHAPTER 33

'Developing awareness is watching carefully what you experience, and accepting that experience, whatever it might be. For example, did anyone feel a change in temperature?' One or two hands went up. One woman felt herself getting warmer, another felt suddenly chilly over her shoulders.

'Then that's what you experienced, and that's what you report back when I ask you if you were aware of anything.'

'But that's hardly mediumship,' said Bob, quite reasonably.

'Of course it's not,' said Hillary, 'but it's the start of mediumship. Until you are aware of what is going on in yourself, you can hardly be expected to be aware of someone else.' She clasped her hands in her lap. What were you aware of during those five minutes? ... apart from nothing!'

'It was hard to keep my thoughts still.'

'So you were aware of your own lively mind?'

'Yes, you could say that.'

'Anything else?'

'A mish-mash of things. Snippets of that old song 'Around The World In Eighty Days'. A packet of Embassy Regal with the red stripe, things to do with my work.'

'I could accept some of that.' All eyes turned towards a carefully made up woman in her fifties - Joyce I think her name was. 'The first film my husband took me to was 'Around The World in Eighty Days' with David Niven,' she said, 'in the Embassy Cinema.'

She's just making this fit, isn't she?' Bob shot his question to Hillary.

'Don't think anything at all,' she said restfully, 'just tell me a few more details of the mish-mash running through your mind. You needn't look at Joyce - she might encourage you or put you off. Just tell me some more,' she said, focusing a little beyond him.

'A black leather wallet with a ten shilling note inside, and a postcard from the Isle of Man,' said Bob distantly as if he were watching it on the opposite wall.

'Our first holiday was in the Isle of Man,' said Joyce, 'and I still have the wallet. He kept the ten shilling note as a memento because it was not legal currency in Britain.... Oh, that's lovely!' she said.

Bob coughed and his eyes seemed to water a little. 'Damn it! I'm nearly in tears,' he said, turning his attention to Joyce this time, ' but I feel really proud I've got through to you. If this man really is your husband, he's just overwhelmed with emotion and really pleased to see you.' As Bob subsided into silence, Joyce radiated pleasure as she smiled. Hillary approached a rather shaken Bob with a glass of water.

'It's OK. Just sip this. You're just more aware than you think you are.' He accepted the glass without a word.

Hillary returned her attention to the group. 'Well done Bob. Life's full of little surprises, isn't it? Now, not all of you will pick up impressions like that, but all of you will have experienced something, no matter how trivial it seems at first. Let's hear how a few of you did.'

She picked this one and that one from the group and listened to their impressions, always reinforcing that each impression was as valid as any other, the important thing was simply to experience and report back as accurately as you could. She talked about 'giving off' impressions as soon as you received them.

'Nothing more will come unless you do,' she said. 'So if you hold on to an impression, a name, a few words or whatever, because you're waiting for something more impressive to follow, you'll find yourself thwarted and disappointed. You really do need to 'go with the flow' in this kind of development.' She turned the music on again and let it play for a few moments without saying anything.

'Close your eyes once again, and slip back into that sea of energy once again. Allow the music to encourage you back into that restful but watchful state. Take five minutes like you did before and then I'll ask each of you to share what you experienced. Remember to expect nothing and to accept everything .....'

This time the exercise was wasted on me. I couldn't help thinking about Bob's experience. What did he do to get those impressions? How did he receive them? Did they feel different from his own thoughts? How would they fit into his world of the Social Sciences? Would he develop his mediumship? When I achieved the well nigh impossible and cleared my mind of thoughts for a microsecond or two and the picture of an old bus ticket flitted through my mind, I panicked in case it meant something - but what? That it was intended for someone - but for whom? That it was all in my imagination and that I was being a fool. I was tense and on edge and disgruntled.

Once again the music faded into silence and the circle was invited to share its impressions. Bits and pieces of impressions here and there could be accepted by members of the circle. Other students offered their experiences which were accepted for what they were. One or two students seemed to be truly in tune with something that allowed them to give descriptions and memories which could be accepted in detail.

I confessed to my failure, giving my account of how curiosity and then paranoia overtook any ability I had to be intuitive.

'But there's always something to learn from everything,' Hillary responded. 'And we're all going to learn from your experience,' she declared, sensing a teaching point in the offing.

'I mentioned the importance of your state of mind early on in the session. At that point, I emphasised Aspiration - aiming for the highest and the best. At the risk of sounding like a business training manual, there are another two A's to consider. One is Adaptability. Your attitude has to be adaptable, or flexible to the impressions you might receive. Never stick with rigid expectations!

'The last A is Acceptance. During the development circle, accept what comes. Don't attempt to analyse or justify it. Say, "I have received this," or, "I have received that - very good." Don't say, "I have received this, but is it true?" or, "I have received that but how did I do it?" You are working with your intuitive mind. It is therefore essential that you allow it to flow without inhibition or restriction. Don't interrupt it: let it flow away!

'There is a time for analysis, reasoning, logic,' she continued. 'It is after the development session is over. Once it's all closed down, that's the time to reflect on the experience and make of it what you will. Talk it over with friends, debate it, fall out over it if you have to ... but do it after the session is finished. That's the time for left brain activity. The development session is the time for right brain activity. So all you need to do,' she said, turning to me, 'is achieve the self-discipline you need for development. Just remember Analysis comes After. ..... more A's.'

Each student 'fed back' to the circle as a whole. The session was coming to a close but it wasn't yet finished.

'Tell me how the circle's energy feels as you slip back into it,' Hillary said to us. We closed our eyes and 'tuned in'.

'There's less of it,' said a female voice.

'It's still there but it's not as bright,' said another.

'Why do you think that might be?'

'Haven't you just gone back into left brain, analytical activity?' I recognised Colin's voice.

'Yes, but I'm not trying to pick up information intuitively at this point,' came Hillary's gentle reply. 'So using any part of your brain that you choose, can you tell me why there is less energy in the circle now?'

'Because we've been using it up?' a male voice offered this question/answer.

'Exactly. But now we are going to take back our share of the remaining energy. So at your own pace, become aware of your own expanded energy all around you. Reach out to as far as it goes, and lovingly draw it back into yourself again, easily and freely as you breathe in and out at your own pace. ... And when you feel that your light is gathered safely back to yourself, imagine it as a beautiful flame in the centre of yourself. Draw it deep into the centre of yourself and (in a sense) wrap it up and protect it with love. ... any way you like. Good.

'Now, at the end of each development session, you should follow that procedure and end with a prayer or positive affirmation - whatever suits you best. Today we shall close like this..... Great Universal Spirit, for your life, light and love, we thank you. For this time of coming together, for this time of being as one, we thank you. Bless us as we grow towards you, and help us to grow more like you. In your name of love, we pray. Amen.'

'Amen,' echoed round the circle. The room was curiously still. 'When you are ready, become aware again of your body. Feel the chair supporting it. Feel your feet on the floor. Wiggle your toes if you like. Remember you are surrounded by colleagues and friends, and when you are ready, open your eyes and stretch if you want to.'

People stretched, coughed a little, sipped water and began to chat.

'The general guidelines for running a development session like this are sketched out for you on this handout,' said Hillary above the hubbub, handing out A4 sheets of pale blue paper. We'll have some discussion after lunch and perhaps do another session before the final roundup at 4 o'clock. Right, I'll see you back here at two o'clock prompt. Thanks very much.' And another session was ended.

CHAPTER 34

'Look!' said a red haired girl to Iris. 'This salad has been Ganzfelded!'
I joined them in the lunch queue and looked at the dish she was pointing at.
Iris laughed.

'Beth, you could be right. What do you think it's receiving right now?
Thoughts from the chef? Our hunger pangs?'

I butted in. 'Do you mean you've been looking like this salad all morning?'

'Well,' said Beth, pointing at halves of hard-boiled eggs surrounded with a
frill of mayonnaise, 'one or two of us did look rather like that.'

'I thought you looked very fetching wearing your ping-pong balls edged
with cotton wool!' said Iris scooping up some coleslaw and adding a few
cherry tomatoes. 'She was floodlit in red light and then the earphones were
put on,' she explained to me as we proceeded along the table, picking up
lettuce, drumsticks and spiced veg along the way.

'What on earth were you doing?' I couldn't begin to imagine.

'The aim was to get bored,' said Beth helpfully.

'She's right,' said Iris as we all sat down to eat. 'First Beth lay down to
relax on a reclining chair thing. The halved ping pong balls were placed
over her eyes and cotton wool was packed round them (just like the eggs
and the mayonnaise!) before the whole thing was taped to her face. That
was to ensure she couldn't see anything going on. When a steady red light
was shone towards her and she opened her eyes,'

'Safely encased in the ping pong balls!' Beth laughed again.

'She could only see this steady, dull red light everywhere.'

'What did it feel like?' I asked.

'Restful but boring,' she replied, 'because it was the same all the time.
Nothing changed.'

'Then the earphones were added,' Iris went on. 'They played white noise
through them.'

'Were they any good?' I asked.

'Were who any good?' said Beth.

'The group... ' Blank stares met my remark. 'White Noise?'

Again there was laughter amid the salad. 'It's not a group, although it's
quite a good name for one - it's like the sound you get between radio
stations, sort of fuzzy. And that's boring too,' Beth added.

'So what's the point of all this boredom then?'

'The theory is that after a while your brain gets fed up with the monotony of
the unchanging input so it stops paying attention to it. Instead it picks up the
finer signals that it wouldn't normally be aware of.'

'Oh yes?' I said, stabbing a garlic mushroom.

'And that's where I come in,' added Iris.

'Doing what?'

'Well, they let Beth settle for ten minutes. She just lay back and described her impressions as they came and went. I was in another room, and ten minutes into the procedure, I had to look at an illustration - just gaze at it for ten minutes and then stop.'

'I kept yakking on to George (who was the experimenter in our group). He jotted down what I was getting. Then gradually they turned down the white sound and the red light, and waited till I felt back to normal. Everything seemed a bit loud and overstated at first - it was weird.'

'Beth was told to sketch what she thought the picture might look like.'

'Yes, but George also asked me loads of questions about how I felt - did I smell anything - or taste anything - or feel heat or water - and other stuff like that.'

'Anyway, then the three of us got back together to see if Beth picked up my picture during the ten minutes I was sending.'

'And did you?'

'Yes and no,' said Beth as she finished off the last of her french bread.

'She got the impression of the watch face - which was incredible really - and the wide blue sky,'

'And a feeling of dryness - aridity.'

'Oh yes, I forgot that,' said Iris, 'which was pretty good. Excellent in fact, because the picture I was sending was one of those odd ones by Dali - you know - molten watches hanging on leafless trees in a sort of desert with a blue sky.'

We moved on to gateaux and more coffee.

'How did your picture come to mind?' I asked Beth. 'Did it come all at once like a flash of inspiration.'

'No, far from it. There was a load of other junk as well - those were just the bits that fitted! But no, it was as if an image began to come into focus. It would build until it was quite clear and then it would fade out again. Then another thing would begin to emerge, and then it would disappear slowly, and so on. But I never saw the whole picture, or even the way the pieces fitted together.'

'But you did get the pieces, that's the interesting thing, isn't it?'

'Yes, I suppose so. So maybe if I could think a bit less myself, I might 'catch' the telepathy with fewer interruptions.'

'Anyway, if Beth is prepared to do this another twenty nine times and come up with similar quality results, Maggie says it will be statistically significant!'

'What about that!' said Beth, making a face.

114

We strolled outside and were surprised to find it was quite warm and sunny. Trapped inside the conference centre, it was almost as if weather no longer existed. We savoured the fresh air as I gave an account of my group's forays into spirit communication.

'It sounds as if Bob's performance was more 'statistically significant' than he was expecting,' said Iris

'It's the fluke that proves the rule!' came a voice from behind her, as Bob strolled by with Gail.

'Will you have another go this afternoon?' I asked him.

'Don't you think one earth tremor is enough in one day?' he said, coming to a halt.

'It's really shaken him - especially the emotional bit. That's so unlike him - stiff upper lip to the end, aren't you?' Gail was obviously delighted that his world view was being nibbled away at.

'Totally inscrutable and enigmatic, that's me. But even I can change,'

'Really?'

'Completely. If you want a private reading, please contact my agent here,' he solemnly indicated Gail. 'She will furnish you with details of my available times, and of course my current rate.'

We all groaned and followed them back to the conference suite.

CHAPTER 35

I sat beside Julia in the rather ramshackle circle that awaited us in Room 3 with Hillary. Joyce sat down next to me as we waited for the rest to arrive. It wasn't long before Hillary drew us all together by asking for questions.

'How can I speed up my development?' asked an intense woman with long amber earrings.

'What kind of development do you mean exactly?' said Hillary in agony aunt mode.

'I want to be a medium, and I'm getting lots of impressions,' her bangles jangled as she moved her hands, 'but I want to build a stronger link with my communicators.' The jangling stopped.

'OK, and what rate is your development going at at the moment?' Hillary's steadiness contrasted with the woman's intensity.

'It's hard to say.'

'Well, put it another way. When did your mediumship or your sensitivity start developing?'

'I started developing about a year ago, when I joined a local group.'

'Would you allow me to disagree with you, I wonder?'

'I might do,' she said reluctantly.

'You're Trish, aren't you?' She nodded. 'How would you feel if I said to you that you had been developing all your life?'

'I could go along with that.'

'And that all your groupwork is doing is revealing 'the story so far'?' Trish continued to wait for her answer. 'You see, there's no one activity that causes development - it's what you are. You are constantly changing, constantly reacting to new experience. It's the build-up of yesterday's reactions that makes you what you are today. So today's awareness is the result of how you lived the rest of your life. Not just what you did in your group, not just which books you read, what exercises you did .... it's how you reacted to your mother's demands, your children's temper tantrums, the queue in the supermarket, everything in life. Perhaps that's why Buddhists practise mindfulness - they watch their own reactions to all things and try to learn about their true selves through that. So if you need a short answer to your question, it is this - develop and encourage mindfulness in what you do.'

'Wouldn't you recommend any special techniques, like working with music or fasting, chanting or a particular course of study?' You could hear disappointment in her voice.

'You know of all these things already. Use them if they appeal to you. But at the end of the day, they simply provide more experiences for you to be mindful of. Life itself, its disappointment, failure, pain; its joy, love or achievement, will develop you just as much if you are mindful of the effect each has on you.' Trish looked unimpressed.

'I want to speed up the process,' she said again. 'I want to work as a medium. I want to link people with the spirit.'

'Then let nature take its course. Let your development happen alongside your experience of life. Then your sensitivity and awareness will be parallel to your spiritual growth and you will be a balanced and strong individual.' Trish shifted in her seat and crossed her arms. 'I thought this weekend was all about development.'

'It is. And I am attempting to explain the best way to develop is through not straining to develop,' said Hillary, taking time to let her words sink in. She went on, 'If you know you are influenced by those on the other side of life, then you know that you have all eternity to develop, to grow and to find the truth. There needn't be any rush,' she said, and as an afterthought, 'in fact, today that might be our greatest spiritual step forward - to realise that there is no rush, no need to speed things up.' She sat back a little, and waited for the next question.

'If you know you have some potential as a sensitive,' said, Colin, looking first at Hillary and then at Bob, 'what should you do about it?'

'Anything you choose, is the short answer. But my answer is perhaps not as flippant as it sounds.' She looked down and spread her skirt more smoothly over her knees. 'You are not duty bound to do anything if you discover you are clairvoyant or whatever. We've touched on this before, I think. You may choose to ignore it, in which case it will remain latent within you. You may choose to nurture it, in which case you may strengthen and refine your awareness. Where this is the case, this finer awareness may help you live your life more creatively, more effectively, or it may provide guidance or wisdom or even healing for other people.'

'Yes, what do you mean by more creatively?' asked Joyce.

'Many natural intuitives never develop their gift along recognisable psychic or mediumistic lines, but they do use their intuition creatively - as a source of ideas and inspiration. They express that inspiration through their art, writing, inventions or even business ideas. We often talk about idealists. I think true idealists are driven to put their ideas into action because they are motivated by powerful intuition.' Looking at Trish, she added, 'If they hadn't been mindful or sufficiently aware of that inspiration, it might have passed them by completely.'

'To go back to my original question, are those the only options for the budding sensitive then: ignore it, nurture it or re-direct it?' It was Colin again.

'Well, I suppose you could stretch it or sell it. We talked earlier about stretching it, but I would never recommend pushing development of awareness. We're not talking about going to the gym and building muscles here. We're talking about sensitivity which is an infinitely more delicate thing. I think it's important that I should explain this further,' she said, warming to her topic. 'Some of your friends in Maggie's group were following the Ganzfeld Procedure this morning. In a nutshell, they cut out as many physical distractions as possible to allow the brain to pick up finer or quieter signals than normal.'

(Our lunch time conversation was reduced to a sentence!)

'Training to be a sensitive means just that. You practice picking up finer signals. Until that's what you start to do. "What's the problem?" you might say. Well, the problem is just that. You pick up the pain of the man sitting next to you. You see a woman is smiling but you feel the malice in her. Once, the fact that a third of the world is starving never bothered you. Now it does. And so it goes on. In five minutes at work you feel the anger in boss, the frustration of the secretary, the depression of the sales manager envelopes you and the greed of a colleague comes at you like hot breath. Where are you in all of this?' she asked the circle. 'Tempest tossed. Your feelings are on the verge of being out of control. And you're not even sure which of the feelings you experience belong exclusively to you. You become easily tired, thin skinned, emotionally drained. Or at least all this could happen to you unless you learn patience, tolerance, self-awareness and (yes) the wise maturity that self discipline and mindfulness encourage.

'Believe me,' she said with a smile. 'Stretching your development isn't worth it. I know. I've been there. Take your time.'

'And what about selling it?' asked Colin. 'Isn't that what you're doing?'

'I'm glad I like you, Colin,' she said with a wry smile. 'Right now, I am not saying to you, "Here is my sensitivity, pay for it." I hope I am saying, "Here is your sensitivity, nurture it." But I must face the fact that you,' she indicated the circle with an outstretched hand, 'are paying me in the same way you pay any teacher. And if you come to me for a reading, you are paying me in the same way you pay any hairdresser, consultant or therapist - for the service I give you. Is that selling my sensitivity? I would rather say that was employing my sensitivity.

'No,' she went on. 'Right now I am not selling my sensitivity. But I run the risk of selling it. And so do you. You or I sell our sensitivity when we use it solely to give others what they want - when we use it only to read fortunes, only to glimpse the future, only to give factual evidence of survival after death, only to impress an ever-growing audience, only to make a living.

'It's important for you to understand that it is not a commodity determined by the rules of supply and demand. Sensitivity should always be a spontaneous human response. There should be times when you do not respond to a demand. There should be times when a client asks for his future and you talk instead about his past. You must keep your sensitivity as free as possible from the demands of your consumers. You are not intended for consumption. You are intended for transformation. People will come to you to be changed. Your sensitivity will help them to change themselves.'

Julia burst out into spontaneous applause, and then blushed for doing so, despite the others joining in.

'Oh dear me,' said Hillary, 'another question, another soap box. Let's get back to work!'

CHAPTER 36

And back to work we went.

'Let's just do a re-cap of what we've covered so far,' said Hillary. 'You've learned to still your mind. You've learned to be watchful of impressions passing through that mind. You've learned to accept what comes to mind without question, and to relay it as it flows. You've also learned that after the circle work is over, you can question and analyse as much as you like. Have you learned anything else?'

'That mediumship is passive,' said Bob. 'You don't set out to get something. You just wait for what comes.'

'Yes, that's good. Anything more?' she looked around the group.

'How to run a development group,' said a lady in velvet.

'Of course, so you can carry on working in your own space and at your own pace when you leave here. Good.' The teacher was pleased.

'Energy,' I said. 'We've learned that we are like energy fields and that when we sit together the energy intensifies and heightens what sensitivity we have.'

'And that we provide our own environment for psychic work. We need to care for each other and work for each other,' Julia chimed in.

'Yes. That can be the difficult bit sometimes. The bit we need to work at remembering,' said Hillary with a smile. 'We've learned quite a lot just sitting around, haven't we?'

'I think I've learned that psychic awareness is not the same as spiritual development. At first I thought it might be,' said Colin.

'You're right,' said Hillary approvingly. 'Psychic awareness often comes as a spin-off from spiritual development, but it has other sources too. And spiritual development may come as a spin-off of psychic development, but it doesn't always happen that way.

'Now, let's begin our last session.' We looked at her expectantly. 'Julie pointed out that our working environment is hugely important, so for this last session, I'm going to emphasise positivity. I'm going to work with several of you to encourage the best results possible.'

She picked out Julia and Bob and the velvet lady whose name was Petra. They sat in a row beside her.

'Now,' she said, 'all I need you to do is sit quietly until you are aware that someone is with you. If no one is there, that's fine. Just let me know.' Looking at the rest of us she continued, 'We call this getting a link. It might be more appropriate to say perceiving a link, but never mind.' She watched her three students sit quietly and close their eyes. Turning back to us, she said,' As you grow more confident, you will sense when a sitter has a link.

You may even see the energy around them as I can do now with Petra and, yes, Bob. Some of you may sense the atmosphere around them has changed. Can you do that?' Some people nodded. I felt that somehow the atmosphere around them was busy. Maybe that's what she was talking about. Then, gazing at Julie, I felt there was a faint shadow behind her. I looked over at Hillary who caught my eye and nodded.

'Julia, dear. Come and stand by me.' Julia did as she was told and Hillary stood with the open palm of her left hand about three inches from her spine. 'Now, dear. Tell me what you've been getting.'

'Well, I'm not sure,' she began.

'That's fine, just tell me anyway.'

'I think there's a man here. He could be in his late forties,' she hesitated, 'but I'm not very good with ages. Maybe he could be up to sixty - ish.'

'Right. You're doing fine. What does he look like?'

Julia gave a slightly muddled description, and when asked, thought he might have been a plumber.'

'Right, Julia,' said Hillary. 'Stay with me as I look at all this. Firstly,' to the audience 'can you see how, as teacher, nothing is denied and each response is encouraged? Why do I do that, do you think?'

'To keep her feeling positive,' I suggested.

'That's right.' Julia smiled a little wanely. 'Does anyone recognise the description so far?'

'I might do,' said Betsy - a lady two along from me.

'But you're not sure,' Hillary expanded.

'Yes,' came the reply.

'Would you be less unsure if Julia had said - I have a man here in his mid forties. He has black wavy hair going grey at the sides, a tanned complexion, heavy eyebrows and blue-grey eyes. He was a plumber to trade?'

'He sounds like my uncle,' said Betsy.

'Yet you said all those things, didn't you?' Hillary turned back to Julia.

'Yes, more or less.'

'And that's just the problem! You see, when you are working, especially at first, you're really not sure what you're talking about.' There was a murmur of agreement around the group. 'So you fudge it all slightly, in case you're wrong.' She looked around us. 'No-one wants to make a fool of themselves. No-one wants to be wrong. But you'll never sound right until you say what your impressions are with confidence. So,' and she gave Julia a little hug here, ' you don't say "I think I'm getting....", you say, "I have ...". You don't say, "he could be in his late forties but ...." you say "he is in is late forties". You'll soon find out if you're wrong, but think how good you'll feel if you're right!' She looked at Julie and said, 'And you were right.

121

Good for you. Now tell me something more about this man.'

'I think I've lost the link,' said Julie, scared of not living up to her new-found success.

'Then find it again,' came the reply with no sympathy and no letting off the hook. The group empathised with her. We didn't know if we'd be in the next batch!

Julie went quiet for a moment as Hillary again stood close to her, her hand at her back. 'Just give the first thing that comes to you,' she encouraged.

'Salt. There's something about salt. I can feel the tang of it in my mouth, as if I was on the sea. Was this man a sailor?'

'What are you asking questions for dear?' Hillary asked softly. 'Stay positive, remember.'

'This man was a sailor in his younger days,' Julia ventured bravely.

'Yes. He was,' said Betsy, 'he was a ...'

'No, no! That's called 'feeding the medium' and you're not allowed to do that. Remember, Julia is here to work for you. All you need to do is support her - send her love and approval - as much as you can!'

'He was in the merchant navy, but he gave up,' said Julie, engrossed now, 'because ... because he got married and wanted a more settled life.'

'Yes, that's right,' said the well-trained Betsy.

'Good for you! Do you see what being positive is doing for you?' said Hillary cheerfully. 'How do you feel about your achievement?'

'I'm pleased,' said Julia. 'Pleased and surprised. In fact I can hardly believe it.'

'Would you like to stop now?'

'Yes.'

'Isn't it terrible how frightening success can be?' teased Hillary as she allowed Julia to sit down.

She worked along the same lines with Bob and Petra, continually reminding them to be positive and uncluttered in what they were saying. Finally she concluded.

'Be like the Quakers,' she said. 'Let your yea be yea and your nae be nae. Don't clutter up your communication with ifs and buts and woolly qualifications. Keep it simple. If you do that, you may be surprised at how clear the message is, and how acceptable it is to your sitter.' She thanked her 'victims' and allowed them back to their places.

'I can only start you off on a two day course like this. Just give you some tools and approaches to work with in the hope that if they appeal, you might work with them and watch your own potential develop. Some of you may develop psychic ability, others mediumship. But some of you will develop insight - it doesn't produce information for other people to marvel at, but it will give you a clearer understanding of people and events. That's worth nurturing too.' She picked up a bundle of paper.

'I hope you have enjoyed your time with us and that you have found it productive. Just before you go, perhaps you would be so good as to complete this feedback form and include whether you would like to attend a further weekend of development. Our paths may cross again - who knows!'

It seemed a particularly low key way to complete the weekend, and before we knew it we were back in the main conference area, milling around watching the New Age stalls being dismantled and swapping phone numbers with the friends we had made.

CHAPTER 37

As we drove home, Iris was telling me about her attempts to predict the fall of coins and the turn of cards - red/black, odd/even and so on.

'So I don't think I'll ever make my fortune with gambling,' she said as she manoeuvred her way in and out of the one-way system.

'Come now, that's negativity.' I said. 'Positivity is the name of the game! Accept your inspiration knowing that it is meaningful to you....'

She laughed. 'OK. I accept that my inspiration is telling me it will not be used for financial gain! Is that acceptable to you oh great guru?'

'Well, for the moment, I shall allow a compromise, but remember the fuller life is awash with challenges tempting you on to greater success....'

'Oh dry up!' came the reply in a friendly tone of voice. We stopped at some traffic lights, and I listened to the engine hum. 'I liked the stuff on dreams though,' Iris moved into gear as the lights changed. 'Apparently, we all have prophetic dreams, but the prophetic bits are mixed in with all sorts of other rubbish. The trick is to note your dreams carefully and keep a record of even the smallest details that come true. There's this guy John Dunne who wrote a book called 'An Experiment With Time' in the 1930s and it's all about how he traced prophecy in the most ordinary dreams.'

'Couldn't that just be coincidence?'

'I'll tell you after I've read the book - if I can find it,' she said, turning into her own road.

'Oh yes, I forgot you were becoming the psychic detective. This is going to be your first case, is it?'

'One of several, my dear Watson. With a criminal mind like mine, one has to keep fully occupied!'

Suddenly we were back in the real world. Rumble had his woolly paws on the side window of her car, the kids followed enthusiastically while Peter and Tom looked on with amusement.

'What, no fish?' I cried amidst the chaos.

'Nothing worth mentioning,' Peter said laconically as Ricky pulled his Mum into the kitchen. 'Only this,' he said producing a two pound trout from behind his back, 'And this,' added Tom with another. 'And what about this?' Ricky was bright with excitement as he produced the final fish from the fridge. It must have been four pounds in weight.

'Wow! Who caught that?' said Iris, knowing the answer already.

'Well, Dad had to give me a hand to reel it in and net it, but I did! I really caught it Mum!'

'And I put it in the fish bag,' said Elsa, not to be left out, 'even although it was all cold and clammy and dead.'

'Well, you were very brave,' I said, giving her a hug. 'I'm glad I didn't have to do that. I'd have dropped it or something.'

'I had to wash my hands afterwards though.'

'And use lots of posh handcream at home to get rid of the smell,' added Tom.

We all piled into MacDonald's to celebrate.

'Can you tell the future now, Mum?' asked Ricky, peering over the top of a huge carton of Coke. Iris pinched one of his chips.

'Oh I think I'll need to put in a lot of practice before I can get that right.' She wiped some sauce from the side of her mouth.

'Tell me where we're going to live next!' he demanded.

'Don't you like living in Manchester then?' She looked from Ricky to Pete who wore an 'I know nothing' look.

'Yes, but we won't be there forever, will we? So tell me where we'll be next.'

'Timbuktu, or Casablanca perhaps.'

'No. A proper prediction!' he demanded.

'Ayr,' I said without thinking.

Ricky looked at me and then his Dad.

'You're right!' he said, putting down the remains of his burger. 'How did you know?' There was a look of astonishment on his face, matched only by the look on Pete's.

'Know what?' I asked blankly.

'What made you say Ayr?' said Pete, looking bemused.

'First thing that came into my head,' I said, frantically looking for a reason or an excuse.

'We're going to Ayr?' Iris was unbelieving. 'Pete, what are we talking about?'

'A breath of air. That's what the clairvoyant said. Do you remember?'

'Pete ...'

'Iris - don't you remember?' I asked.

'Remember? Sorry, what are you talking about?' By now she was bewildered and it was catching.

'Saturday night. The clairvoyant - John - remember? He said you'd move and Marjorie said something about a change of air or something. That's why I said Ayr.'

'You were talking to grandma?' Ricky blinked and stopped sucking at his straw.

'Hold it! Stop right there!' Iris placed both splayed hands carefully on the table top in an attempt at control.

'Peter, are we really moving to Ayr?' This time she wouldn't be distracted.

'Yes, dear.' He was sheepish now.

'Why?' she was seriously into self control by now.

'Morris phoned.'

'Who's Morr...?' I stage whispered.

'Boss,' she fired back, concentrating on Pete.

'The research job,' he smiled. 'I got it. It was supposed to be a surprise.'

'You got it?' would she laugh or cry, I wondered. Now Elsa, Ricky, Tom and I were doing a sort of Wimbledon Centre Court sort of thing between the two of them. Back to Pete.

'Yes. With special responsibility for Scotland - hence Ayr. They're based there.' he added helpfully, beginning to smile as he assessed her mood. Over to Iris.

'And the salary?' she looked as if she was waiting for the last number for a full house. Back to Pete.

'What we talked about,' he looked prouder than Ricky with the fish now.

'Yes!' She jumped up to give him a hug. So did we. The whole table applauded as the other customers looked on mystified. 'That's wonderful! That's really wonderful! Why didn't you tell me on Saturday?'

'Because it was a surprise,' said Elsa. 'You like surprises.'

'Then let's have knickerbocker glories all round to celebrate!' said Tom. 'I'll pay.'

As her Mum and Dad chatted excitedly about timescales and house prices, Elsa tugged my sleeve. She looked up at me very seriously. 'Will we have a house on the sea shore?' Ricky was listening intently. I looked at Tom, lost for words in my new role as prophetess. He leaned towards the children. 'Well now,' he said. 'You must make a choice.' They looked at him, wide eyed. 'You can have a prophecy or a knickerbocker glory, but,' he was very serious now, 'you can't have both. What's it to be?' He drew their attention to the tall glasses lined up on the counter. They were just adding the chocolate sauce.

Elsa's face lit up. 'Knickerbockers!' she declared with authority. And my crisis was over!

CHAPTER 38

Once home from MacDonald's, Tom and I hastily packed up our belongings (including a carefully wrapped-up fish) and squeezed them into the
back of the green MX5. We were a little later in setting off for home than
we had planned, but we had promised our dog-sitters that we'd be back
about ten on Sunday night, so we felt duty bound to be on our way.

We were waved off with promises of regular bulletins on the progress with
houses and jobs and (of course) psychical research.

'Thanks for saving me from a second prophecy,' I said to Tom as we found
ourselves safely on the motorway.

'I didn't want you to lose your reputation so soon after gaining it,' he said.

'It was an impressive turn. Are you going to make a habit of it?' The city
lights faded behind us.

'Not if I can help it. I've got enough responsibilities without adding that to
my repertoire.'

'Responsibilities? I thought you were as free as a bird, carefree and
footloose. What responsibilities?' The cats' eyes on the road flashed past as
he picked up speed.

'Looking after you of course, and telling you to turn your wipers on.'

'Oh, yes, it is raining, isn't it?'

'And offering you something to chew?' I rustled a bag of sweets in his
direction.

'No thanks. Not after that meal!'

'And getting this radio to work. I tell you, I'm overwhelmed with
responsibilities!' Our conversation drifted as I found a station which didn't
sound as if it was on fire.

Riding along in the dark, with the music playing softly, I let my mind wander
over the weekend and the experiences it brought. From time to time I'd
share an anecdote with Tom and then slip back into the sleepy darkness.

The road seemed long, and nearly two hours later, as we left the outskirts of
Dumfries, I resigned myself to the slow, winding section of the journey.

I remember seeing the sign for Dunscore, and the light from headlights at
the junction. The light kept on coming. Tom swore as the landscape spun.
Force and sound became one as the night caved in. Down, down I went,
into a sticky wet darkness, looking for Tom, calling out for him, unable to
see.

Where did the light go? I reached beyond tangled metal, seeing nothing but
knowing it was there. I felt my way round the outside of the car. It was wet
Braille telling me its story. There was a groan. I moved towards it. The
driver's door. Where was the handle? I couldn't find it. Tom mumbled a
mantra of oh my god, oh my god. I could hear him but couldn't see him.
Rain like stair rods beat on the uneven bonnet.

'Get help,' I thought. 'I can't stay here. I must get help. I can't see, can't feel. I must get help.' Something hissed. A car radiator perhaps. Metal creaked against metal. Fear turned me over as if my body vomited my soul. 'Help. I need help,' I thought.

Through the dark I moved. Through the rain and felt nothing. Running, always running. Powered by panic.

'Slow down. It's OK. We've got you!' Arms, dry arms, broad chest, warm and dry. I sobbed into it, clutching the fabric.

'There's been an accident. You've got to help. I need help!' The power in my legs seeped away and I felt myself falling.

'It's OK. We've got you.' Same voice. Strong arms. Carrying me. 'You're safe,' it said. I couldn't see, but I could feel light on my face as I was laid on the bed, warm, dry, safe. The air was sweet. I unwound and slept into a dream. Faces looked down at me. Warm, reassuring. Mum held my hand gently on the counterpane. Her other hand swept hair off my forehead. 'You're going to be fine, love,' and she faded. Family faces came and went like passing cameos. Then, who knows how long after, 'Follow me,' said a voice that was familiar and I slipped out from between the sheets and walked through open windows into the fresh air of a garden.

The light was bright against my unsure eyes, but as I focused I could see grass and trees. 'Where's Tom?' I asked the figure in front of me.

'Don't worry, he's waiting for you.'

'Sybil?' I peered through the light, disbelieving. I followed the figure round a large tree where it found a bench to sit down on. She looked younger than when I last saw her, but perhaps it was the light. She patted the bench.

'Sit down and talk. You've been through a lot.' I touched the bench to check out how real it was.

'Sybil, am I dreaming?' I sat down carefully.

'No,' she said with a smile. 'If anything, you are more aware than normal.' In a sense, she was right. As I grew used to the light and the open air, I could feel her tenderness and support - almost taste it - if that doesn't sound crazy. I looked around, trying to recognise something familiar.

'Where is this place? Is Tom here?' I searched her face for answers. 'How did I get here anyway?'

'You're in the afterlife,' she said, taking my hand and watching me steadily.

'Oh no!' I said drawing my hand from hers, 'Oh no! you're not giving me that. Not that. I'm conscious, I have a body, I can feel. You can't tell me I died, you can't...' Tears ran down my face. I was faint with disbelief, reeling in confusion. I would have run away if I could have.

Sybil was holding both of my reluctant hands now. 'Who was with you in the recovery area?' she asked softly.

'Why, my mother and ....' A leaden chill filled me. Mum died seven years ago. I leant over and sobbed against Sybil. 'I don't understand,' I blurted.

128

'How can I be alive and dead at the same time?' She held me silently until the tears subsided.

'Your physical body suffered the trauma,' she said, nursing me, 'not your spirit. When the body can't cope any more, the spirit is freed. It lives independently - like this - like I am now.'

I sat up tensely. 'Like you are now .... And me? Am I like you now?' There was something in her tone of voice.

'That's your choice,' she said, stroking me lightly as if I were a child.

'I've got a choice? Can I go back? ... You said Tom was waiting for me? Where is he?'

'At your bedside in the hospital,' she said. 'Look.' And as I looked at her, our scenery changed. She was still looking at me, but we were above a group in a hospital. I saw the bed, a body lying on it, wreathed in bandages. To the right was the life support machine, and behind it a drip. Tubes were everywhere - at the nostrils, taped to the arm. One leg was plastered, so it seemed, and slightly suspended. A seated figure leaned over the body. A crutch leaned on the bed. On the other side a woman sat quietly, patiently and I could see light around her.

'Look closer at the patient,' said Sybil. It was me. It was my body lying on the bed. And yes, Tom was there waiting, leaning over anxiously. He said something I couldn't hear and Mhairi replied.

'How can I be two places at once?'

'Your body,' said Sybil indicating the bed, 'and your spirit,' pointing to me.

'It's touch and go. You lost a lot of blood ...'

'But I ran,' I said incredulously. 'I ran to get help.'

'You left your body,' she corrected. 'Your spirit left your body. You nearly died. You're still borderline.' She looked at my face. 'Going back will be tough. One lung is punctured. There are fractured ribs, a broken leg, damaged pelvis ... there could be complications.'

'But I have the choice,' I said. I looked at Tom's face. His heart was written there. Mhairi would help - was helping. 'I have the choice,' I said again, to make it real for me, to make it possible. 'I have the choice.'

I moved slowly towards the body on the bed. Every inch I moved closer I felt heavier, darker, more confined. Closer still.

'The monitor!' exclaimed Tom. 'Look!'

Closer still to feel the heat and then the pain.

'The pulse is stronger,' said Mhairi.

Closer still to begin the hard labour of breathing with the world's weight on my chest. Just before the cellar door closed on me I saw the tears in Tom's eyes.

'I think she's rallying,' said Mhairi. The choice was made.

CHAPTER 39

Into the Immortality Business.

As the biological clock ticks away and the have-it-all generation has had it all, what happens next? Slippers by the fire? A life on the internet? Or an unlimited extension of the 'me' experience? Colin Parker investigates.

In a plush city hotel, on a quiet weekend, one New Age Psychic Development Seminar promised it all - extended sensitivity, new ways of knowing and spiritual growth, all washed down with a good sales pitch for eternal life. Maybe I was missing something. I went along and enrolled as a student to see for myself.

Seeing Clearly Incorporated is the business venture of Maggie Curdy and Jill Stoddart, both psychic consultants to trade. Maggie is a plump but well presented fiftysomething with a background in administration. Her partner Jill who is married and in her thirties, left a sales career for psychic consultancy when stress and pressure threatened to stifle her gift. 'Starting the consultancy with Maggie gave me the opportunity to follow my own pathway instead of someone else's,' she said when I asked her about her involvement. 'Having developed our awareness over the years, we are able to give meaningful help and guidance to people who are facing life problems. I get real satisfaction from that,' she said. As well as £120 per head for the weekend seminar.

Asked whether she agreed that guidance from psychics wasn't the most reputable method for facing life's challenges, Maggie replied, 'We're professional, that's the difference. We offer an alternative view to our clients and make a point of recommending they take on real personal responsibility as they choose how to use the information.' So there were no strings attached.

When they're not seeing into your future or reading your character, they focus their attention on 'helping you realise your inner potential'. (I'm tempted to offer, 'Opening your wallet,' as the alternative in materialist-speak.)

Your 'inner potential' is apparently enclosing your ability to give psychic readings and exercise a variety of forms of ESP - extra-sensory-perception. It needs unlocked, and Maggie and Jill are the ladies to do it. The key to your realisation may lie in the variety of books, self-help packs and New Age Clutter available from their Treasure Trove (shop) set up in the main seminar area. I have to say, it came as something of a shock to realise that according to its accumulated 'treasure', I was variously: reincarnated, in need of re-birthing, ready to be crystal healed, protected

130

by angels and condemned for the way my ancestors treated Red Indians. If I bought a prayer flag, it might help. As yet unrealised, I declined.

Perhaps a particular set or tarot cards would 'speak' to me, suggested an assistant, or if I listened I might feel a kinship with one of the crystal balls. 'Balls,' I repeated, meditatively. (Wouldn't you?) At £30 per item I was deaf and blind. But I was intrigued by what brought so many people (about 60) to such an event. Over the two days I met a jeweller, an accountant, a company director, a restaurant owner, a single mum, a lecturer and a computer salesman. Quite a cross section, and all happy to be there.

Maggie may have had her finger on the pulse when she talked about 'life problems'. About half the clients/students, were inevitably middle aged and no doubt experiencing the flavour of that particular crisis, but as conversations blossomed over coffee, flavoured water and herb tea, I caught more than a fair share of comments about bereavement, redundancy, early retirement, broken relationships, problem children & parents and crises in business. Had the liberation of the Sixties and Seventies come home to roost? I wondered. A lot admitted to looking for some sort of comfort or direction - two luxuries denied to them since the decline of orthodox religion in society. Some felt they'd lost their way or their identity in life. Serious stuff for a Saturday morning.

How classes in Telepathy or Sensing Colour were going to sort out all these problems, I hadn't quite mastered at that early stage, but I was willing to learn. While my assistant sleuth went off to sample the thrills of realising her 'Psychic Potential', I braved 'The Spiritual Aspect' in the beginners' group where I met the two guest workers : John and Hillary for the first time. Both were mediums. John had worked in the hotel business prior to going full time as a clairvoyant. He was casual and relaxed, giving the impression he could have been a sports commentator. Hillary on the other hand, in her sixties, wore an air of authority easily, despite claiming nothing more for herself than 'natural mediumship'. I suspect between them, they sold fewer of the Treasure Trove's wares than their colleagues did.

Instead they sold the idea that it all boiled down to 'energy'. (The new religion.) You and I are essentially 'bundles of energy'. You and I can sense different kinds of energy - plants, crystals, colours and (yes) people. We can heal people by sending energy to them. We can understand people better by 'tuning in' to their personal energy. We can even 'tune in' to the energy of those who have passed on and 'no longer have a physical body'. We are all part of the great universal energy, and the more we realise that, the more that energy will work through us and look after us. (The new god.)

It looked like I had the answer to all my life problems. Except I

131

still had to learn how to get in touch with that energy and use it. That's where 'development work' (The new ritual.) comes in. As students (disciples) we spent a lot of time stilling our minds and watching for the impressions we received (or getting nowhere in my case).

But not everyone drew a blank like me. Recently widowed, Joyce remained convinced that her dead husband communicated with her through impressions one of the students received - a collection of memories from their courting days. And maybe she was right. Certainly, her budding medium, Bob, was as shocked as any of us to find that what was running through his mind might be coming from another mind completely. Starting off as a very verbal cynic, he became considerably quieter as the weekend wore on.

'It could be coincidence,' he said rather unconvincingly,' or perhaps telepathy works and I picked up what Joyce wanted to hear. I'll need to think about that. I felt very emotional as I spoke to her, and that's not like me.'

'Could you have been sensing her energy?' I asked, feeling more at home with the new jargon.

'How do you do that?' he asked. 'I certainly wasn't trying to do anything at all.' So maybe he was gifted, or intuitive, I suggested. 'Who knows?' was the reply.

As students we were led through this wonderland of new experience - breaking down boundaries between individuals, between life and death, like it happened all the time. The new theology is that in this universal soup of energy, we are born, become individualised, cast off the physical body at death and continue to live as personalities in an afterlife with pleasing landscapes. With an eternity to do it in, we've plenty of time to become the together people - the realised potential - we dream about.

And the new priesthood? On Saturday evening when Maggie, Jill and John gave their 'demonstration of clairvoyance' to an audience of over two hundred, their claim to be the go-betweens in this heaven and earth scenario - mediums bearing messages from the after-lifers - placed them firmly in that role. Characters were described (some more specifically than others), memories shared and advice given.

Was it all real? Prior to the meeting, one woman said she hoped there was an afterlife and that it would be confirmed for her. Yes, she said, it would give her a lot of comfort. She didn't think any of the mediums knew anything of her background so she'd be happy to accept what they said as genuine. It was her friend who interrupted to remind her she had spoken in detail about her mother's death earlier that afternoon.

She got a message.

So did I. The immortality business is alive and well.

CHAPTER 40

'Well, what did you think of the article then?' Tom tapped the paper lying beside me. The first weeks in hospital were a blur to me - people coming and going, tests, medicines, consultants. I was being processed, and sooner or later, I thought, I'd come through it and regain my personality. For the moment I was a list of problems to be solved, however caringly.

Sometimes I remembered snatches of deep conversations with people I'd known and never known. At other times, familiar hands held mine, familiar voices talked of a now unfamiliar world of work, bargains at sales, children and new houses, tax forms and 'news'. I sailed through it on the barge of a broken body laden it seemed with medication.

Colin's article appeared at the time I was harbour-bound - almost ready to land on steady ground again. Almost ready to stop surviving and start getting better. I smiled at Tom, pleased to see him and surprised that I'd actually read the whole thing and understood it!

'You're looking brighter,' he said with an encouraging hug. 'Here's some flowers for you, and some fudge.' He sat down cheerfully and then stood up again. 'Look - no plaster! What do you think?' His ankle had been broken in the crash, but now it was plaster-free.

'That's great,' I said. 'How does it feel?'

'Not bad at all,' he said, sitting down again. 'I only carry this stick around for effect. It inspires sympathy,' he added with a grin. It was good to see and think clearly again. 'So is this Colin a rogue or a cynic or just telling the truth?'

'A bit of all three, I think. Plus a man making a living.' I picked out a cube of fudge for myself, and offered the bag to Tom. The sweetness was delicious. 'I think he was more impressed with Hillary than he shows here, but it's hard to say. Iris was the woman who got the message, did she say?' He shook his head. 'And I was the interrupting friend. So he was absolutely accurate with that. But what he couldn't know was just how accurate was some of the detail John gave. Iris did talk about Marjorie, but not what her initials were, nor about the things we experienced as she died. Only we knew that. Remember I told you? Colin couldn't know how impressive that was just by listening. He'd have had to be on the receiving end. And then there was the prediction about moving. That just sounded wrong to an outsider ..... have they got a house yet?'

'At long last,' said Tom. 'The deal was finalised on Friday, and Elsa's over the moon. You can see the sea from her bedroom window - or so she tells me.'

'When do they move in?'

'The end of next month, so I suspect there'll be plenty of opportunities for baby sitting when you feel up to it!' I warmed to the possibility of a real life again. Simple things like watching children and walking dogs.

'So you see, he was right there too.'

'What do you think of it all? Are they rip-off merchants?' He tucked into the fudge again until I asked if I might have another tiny piece.

'There's an element of that. People like what they can buy, don't they? It's easier than making a change in themselves. Or thinking for themselves. Just let someone else do it for them. But just because people are prepared to spend money finding out about it doesn't mean that it's all a con.'

'You mean just some of it is a con?'

'Yes, I suppose I do .... the merchandising ... the idea that everyone can be supersensitive or in tune with the world after a weekend's worth of development work. Maybe that's more wishful thinking than a con. It's the same reason that anti-wrinkle creams sell.'

'People want it to be true, you mean?'

'Yes. That's why Colin's poking fun at it. Fair enough. But he's looking at it from the outside. Look from the inside and it's different.'

'What do you mean, love?' An auxiliary came and volunteered to put the flowers in water. I told him about my experience of the crash, the apparent running for help, the people I met, the care I received, my conversation with Sybil.

'It was a real choice I made, Tom. I know it was.' He looked searchingly into my face.

'What makes you so sure?'

'There was a point when you knew I would make it, wasn't there?'

'Yes, it was ...' I put my hand up to stop him.

'No, don't tell me,' I said. 'It was just when the monitor started to show a stronger pulse. Mhairi was sitting at the top right of the bed, near the monitor, and you were opposite, seated on a chair further down on the left. Your crutch was leaning on the bed. She was wearing that heavy Norwegian sweater of hers and you were in some dressing gown I've never seen before.'

'That's right,' he said, 'but how could you have known that? You hadn't regained consciousness then.'

'Your eyes filled with tears as you saw the change,' I said. 'I know because I was watching you as I came closer and closer.' Now it was my turn to feel choked up. 'That's when I decided I was coming back.' He perched on the bed and cradled me softly backward and forward.

'It's OK, it's OK. I love you too,' he murmured.

'Is everything all right?' The auxiliary came back with the flowers.

'Yes, yes. Everything's one hundred per cent OK,' he said into my hair, and then, 'We're just fine, honestly,' to her anxious face.

Colin's article was a reminder of where I had left off. In a sense, I felt I could pick up from there and move on now. If I had really seen that room the way it really was when I was unconscious, then (to me at least) I had really slipped into the next phase of life, really been with Mum again, really shared my thoughts with a Sybil who was real. I felt a new confidence in me.

Later on, when visiting time was over, I laid back on my pillows and thought that I would never be afraid of dying - I'd virtually done it already! I hadn't bought the idea of an afterlife : I'd experienced it. I couldn't prove it to anyone else. I didn't need to. I didn't need to prove it to me either.

'It's like the taste of strawberries,' I thought. 'While someone else tells you about it, it means nothing at all. But once you've had that taste - it stays with you forever.'

I snuggled down, aware still of the ache of concussion and throb of still-mending bones. 'Well, I've tasted life proper,' I mused to myself, 'and it's good.'

CHAPTER 41

'Well, you're back.' It was Sybil, leaning against the bench where I was potting seedlings in the greenhouse. The afternoon was heavy and moist as the sun shone through the glass roof. I was perched on an old high stool to prevent me standing too long, and I'd already peeled off a jumper as I worked away. I was still aware of my own clumsiness, but I was gradually getting back to normal.

'After a fashion! I'm not exactly Speedy Gonzalez,' I said, teasing out the fine delicate roots of the little plants. 'Looks like you're back too,' I added with a wry smile, for I hadn't really been aware of her since the accident.

'Mm,' she said, looking around my array of trays and fibre, little knives, sprays and watering cans. 'But now you know I'm not your imagination after all.' Her eyes looked directly into mine.

'Yes, you persuaded me in the end ... but I would have preferred less drastic means,' I added.

'Ah now, that was nothing to do with me. There was no engineering of events going on. You just happened to find your way over to my place.' She smiled and watched as I carried on working, encouraging the seedlings to stand on their own in the moist fibre.

'Do you think I would have come to the same conclusion if I hadn't nearly died?' I asked.

'Yes, eventually, but you would have taken your own time. Use the end of that pencil to make the holes in the fibre. You'll get on better.' Ever bossy, I thought, but I tried her suggestion and it worked. She nodded approvingly and continued, 'You're growing, like these are. They won't flower now, but if you look after them, they will in a month or two. At the right time, in the right season. Sometimes people forget that they're growing too. They panic at change - especially physical change in themselves after maturity - because they fear it's a sign of decay. But growth never happens without some kind of change. Deny that and you'll wear yourself out trying to achieve the impossible of standing still. It's against nature and against your very own nature.' I potted away steadily, thinking about what she was saying. 'The same is true with ideas. You accept an idea that reflects the level of your understanding. But your understanding doesn't stand still. As you gain more insight into something, your concept of it changes. You might think it would be comfortable to hold on to the ideas you once called true, but it's not really. Sooner or later your truth gets uncomfortable. Cling to it despite this and you grow world weary or depressed or anxious.'

'Like these seedlings would be if I didn't separate them out and give them space?'

'Precisely. Be brave enough to let it go or let it grow, and you'll find yourself with a fresh idea that fits your new understanding. Give it space in your life, and it'll grow strong.' I watered in one tray of the seedlings. 'That's the stage you were at just before the accident,' Sybil went on. 'You'd got past the anxious stage and you were making space for the new idea of what you really are, to take root and grow.'

'So the near death experience was a sort of manure that just brought things forward a little!'

'You could put it that way ...'

'A sort of educational shituation ...'

'But I wouldn't put it that way!' She laughed.

'So what happens now?' I asked. 'I've experienced (or nearly experienced) life after death, so the pressure to change the world before I die has lifted a bit.' She smiled ironically. 'I'm drawn to the idea that I'm a spiritual being in a physical body - a 'bundle of energy' like Hillary said. So what do I do now?'

'Live like it.'

'Live like what?'

'You must excuse my grammar. It must be the company I'm keeping. You should live as if you really were spiritual first and physical second. Not the other way round.'

'How do I do that?'

'That's very much up to you,' she said rather smugly.

'I knew you were going to say that!'

'Then you could have saved yourself the effort of asking the question ... but listen to my answer. It's not meant as a rebuff. If you embark on any kind of spiritual life, other people's rules may not suit you. You have to decide. It really is up to you. Will you sacrifice yourself with a life of service? Will you seek self development or self realisation? Will you follow the ancient path of seeking self knowledge? Or make your life an example of goodness in action? You could go into politics. Or put your creativity to good use for the benefit of others - do research, invent something, make a work of art ... or grow some flowers,' she said looking at my afternoon's work.

'I'm back to meditation,' I said, 'but then I suppose you know that. I could join a group or a church or something...' Sybil took a breath. 'I know,' I beat her to it,' it's completely up to me.'

'Well that's an improvement at least! You see, dear, you can call me what you like - angel, spirit guide, etc. But whatever my job description is, it's not to answer your questions. It's to help you answer yourself.'

'Because I couldn't grow otherwise.'

'Exactly. Explore all the possibilities. See which one suits you best just now and pursue it wholeheartedly. But even at your most whole-hearted, remember that today's truth may not be tomorrow's. Always leave a little space for change.'

I swept up the excess fibre into a little mountain and brushed it back into the bag. 'I think I'm seizing up,' I said. 'I think I'll have to move about a bit.'

'Exactly so,' said Sybil with authority. 'Let's go and look at the plants. I like the pots Tom bought you.'

'Oh, those,' I said, struggling to my feet. We put them in the corner where they catch the sun. They're so close to the house, the birds rarely come anywhere near them.'

'And just look under that really dark green leaf,' she said. 'It's just waiting for you.'

With the sun warm on the back of my hand, I carefully leant down to uncover the first of the crop. It's ripe sweetness burst onto my tongue.

'Mmm,' I said, 'strawberries!'